MiniMaths

2

Kim Connor

Published by BEAM Education

Note

The Early Learning Goals listed in the chart on p106 are from the QCA (Qualifications and Curriculum Authority) document *Early Learning Goals*, © Qualifications and Curriculum Authority 1999

ISBN 1 874099 80 4

Introduction by Helen Williams

Illustrated by Kelly Dooley

Designed and typeset by BEAM Education

Printed in England by Brown & Son

British Library Cataloguing-in-Publication Data

A catalogue record for this publication is available from the British Library

Contents

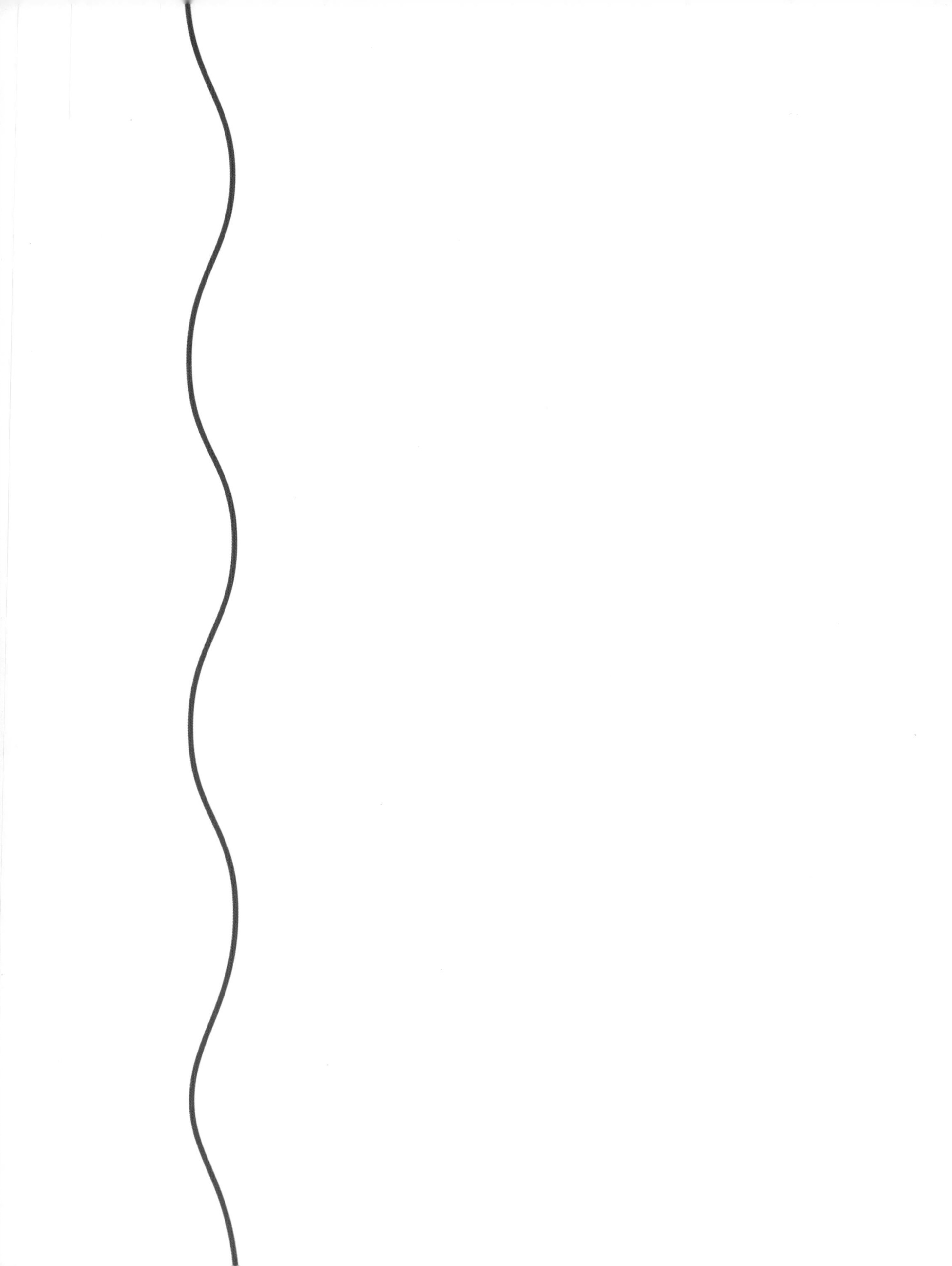

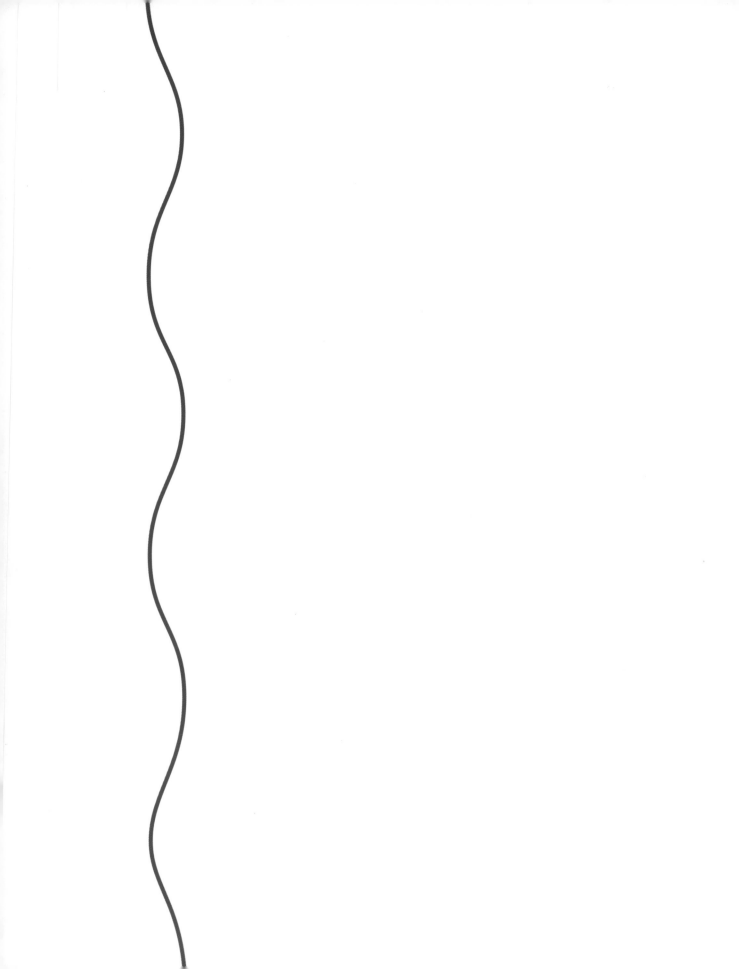

Introduction

MiniMaths is packed with ideas for mathematical activity with young children. It is a resource for adults working with Nursery, Reception or Pre-school children in any early years setting.

Each chapter uses an 'everyday' item such as our hands, or containers, as the basis for a wide range of mathematical activity. This approach has three significant benefits:

- it de-mystifies maths by showing that mathematical activity can make use of whatever is to hand
- it makes clear to children that mathematics is inherent in our everyday practical lives: at home, at school and in the world around us
- it makes use of familiar items to tackle less familiar mathematical ideas

How do children learn?

Mathematical activity needs to take account of the interests and enthusiasms of young children. Children have a natural curiosity about what is around them, and this includes the mathematical. By cutting, drawing, handling items and playing games, young children demonstrate their willingness to become involved in mathematics.

Young children learn through:

- **Play** Children need the opportunity to take control of mathematics in the context of play. Playing with ideas helps children develop the confidence to 'have a go' — and to learn when and where to go for help if necessary.
- **Repetition** Frequent repetition of an enjoyable activity makes it familiar to children, giving a sense of control over the mathematics involved.
- **Communication** Children learn through doing things with others, and in particular by talking to each other and to adults about what is taking place at each stage of an activity. Talk is the link between doing something and knowing something.
- **Observation** It is important to give children the opportunity to watch and listen, both to adults and to each other. It is as appropriate to watch and listen in mathematics as it is in other curriculum areas. When we watch and listen we have opportunities to observe differences and similarities, to share ideas and to use other people's ideas to build on our own.
- **Practical contexts** Mathematics is a mental activity — but mental work must be based on practical activity. Children's mental strategies need to be developed in a variety of contexts that can be 'seen' and visualised.

What children learn at home and school

All young children arrive at their early years setting with a wealth of mathematical knowledge from home that they will bring to bear on their new learning experiences. Future learning has to take account of this knowledge. Talk to families and carers about the maths you and the children are doing, so that they can support their child's mathematics learning at home. Include families and carers by asking them to help collect appropriate resources (egg boxes, cereal packets and so on), or by inviting them to come in and participate in activities. Carers will get a clear picture of the maths their children do in school if they can come in and talk to you and to the children, listen to the songs you sing, and hear the discussions you have and the questions you ask. All of this opens up a mathematical dialogue between children, families and schools.

Curriculum Guidance for the Foundation Stage (QCA, DfEE, 2000) defines stages through which children are expected to progress in the early years. Nursery and Reception teachers will have the QCA's Early Learning Goals in mind as an end point and will plan with regard to the development of the 'whole child'. *MiniMaths* is cross-referenced both to the Early Learning Goals themselves (see the chart on p106), and to significant steps leading up to the Goals (see the chart at the end of each chapter). This is to support you in the planning and assessment of the activities.

Background theory to MiniMaths

MiniMaths is based on a 'talk, do, talk, do again, talk' cycle. It provides:

- structured activities to either precipitate or follow free play, for children to explore and reinforce their own ideas and their own learning
- plenty of opportunities for children to talk about what they are going to do, what they are doing and what they have done

MiniMaths recognises that young children need to learn both to focus on a task alone and to work with others. Some activities begin with children pooling ideas about how to go about something before they work alone, and end with children sharing their results with each other. Others involve children working cooperatively as part of a small group, for example when playing a game.

All the activities are structured around 'open' questions such as: "How can you...?", "How might we...?", "How will you...?". Discussing and solving problems lies at the heart of *MiniMaths*, just as problem-solving lies at the heart of mathematics.

MiniMaths prioritises practical and mental work. Children only make records of their work on paper as an integral part of a task. You might, for example, ask: "How can you remember that?", "Can you show all the combinations you have found?" or "Can you think of a way of keeping track on paper of the ones you have found?"

Ways to introduce MiniMaths

You might choose to spend a week using, say, 'Flowers' as the focal point for your mathematics. Each chapter opens with 'all together', ideas for preliminary activities. 'Let's Sing', 'Let's Do', and 'Let's Investigate' help to introduce the topic. The twelve activities in each chapter cover a broad range of mathematics. In the margins you will find lists of the key vocabulary and the maths learning covered, and the significant steps chart at the end of each chapter provides a more detailed guide to the mathematical content of the activities. Finally, you can match the content of each activity to the Early Learning Goals at a glance by referring to the table on p106.

Each activity can be chosen as it stands for a group of children to do initially with an adult. The activity can then be left out for children to explore in their free play. Alternatively, some of the more structured activities, such as games, might be more successful when preceded by free play with the resources. To ensure that children gain the maximum benefit from the activities, you will need to provide opportunities for them to repeat the tasks, either alone in their play or as part of a group. You can also adapt tasks for children to take home and share with their families and carers. Each activity includes two 'challenges' for the most interested children.

The 'Can the child…' section in each activity lists the assessment points for each activity. It refers not only to mathematics goals, but to the young child's personal, social and emotional development.

Dip in and enjoy your *MiniMaths*!

Helen Williams
early years mathematics consultant

How to use this book

MiniMaths is divided into six chapters. Each chapter contains twelve activities covering a range of mathematical experiences.

The activities can be used flexibly to accommodate the requirements of Nursery or Reception children. Each activity offers two 'challenges', which can be used as extensions for older or more able children.

At the end of each chapter is a chart showing significant steps that we have identified for early years learning. Finally, on p106 you will find a table linking every activity in the book to the QCA's *Early Learning Goals*.

Build a rockery

Give each pair of children the 'stepping stones' to make a track. The children take it in turns to roll the 1–3 dice, pick up a pebble and move it that number of steps along the track. Children must roll the exact number at the end of the track to move into the 'rockery' and then start again with another pebble. Play continues until all ten pebbles are in the rockery.

Things to ask

- How many steps must you take?
- How can you find out how many pebbles there are in your rockery?
- If you have seven pebbles in the rockery, how many more pebbles are there to move?
- If you roll a two, will you reach the rockery?

Challenges

Add more stepping stones and give the children a 1–6 dice.

Give the children two 1–3 dice and challenge them to work out the combined numbers.

Can the child...

Explain how to play the game?

Count the appropriate number of steps?

Say how many more to make ten?

Work cooperatively with a partner?

Flowers

You will need

- ten large paper 'stepping stones' per pair
- ten pebbles per pair
- a 1–3 dice per pair

one, two...
how many?
(not) enough
nearly
count
start at
finish
how many are left?
how many more to make?

Maths learning

Count reliably up to ten everyday objects

Begin to use the vocabulary involved in adding and subtracting

Use developing mathematical ideas and methods to solve practical problems

83

You will need

This lists the resources you will need to provide for the activity.

Key words

These are words you will probably use naturally during the activity. Most of the words are listed in the National Numeracy Strategy's vocabulary list. Others are everyday words used in a mathematical context. For some activities, you may like the children to repeat and use the words themselves; for others, you may choose just to introduce the vocabulary, giving it in a range of contexts for a good understanding.

Things to ask

This gives some ideas for questions to ask, to stimulate the children's thought processes and encourage the use of mathematical vocabulary. Most of the suggestions are 'open' questions, to encourage exploration and develop self-confidence. The questioning might also be used to support children with specific needs.

Challenges

These are suggestions for ways to extend or vary the activity for older or more able children.

Can the child...

This is an assessment checklist for practitioners. It gives you an idea of what to look out for when assessing the children's mathematical understanding and personal and social development.

Maths learning

This section gives you an 'at-a-glance' guide to the mathematics covered in each activity. For a more in-depth guide, please see the Early Learning Goals chart at the end of the book.

Almost anything that's round can be used as a wheel in this chapter — even a potato! Ideas for all-'round' mathematical fun abound! We make prints of wheels and wheel-tracks in paint and describe the patterns and shapes they make. We talk about the differences between 2D and 3D wheel-shapes and think of ways to sort them. We count out wheels or passengers according to the number on a dice, then go on to do some addition and subtraction.

Contents

Wheels

Let's sing

"The wheels on the bus go round and round..."

Sing the song and do the actions. Using chairs or blocks as bus seats, act out getting on the bus, playing all the parts.

Can you think up a part for everyone?

What other vehicles could we sing this song about? "The wheels on the bike...?" "The wheels on the lorries...?"

Let's do

Make a bus stop

Each day ask a different child to stick on the bus stop three different numbers from a pack of 1–20 cards.

Which buses are stopping here today?

Wheels line

Use different wheels, give each a number from 1–10, and string them onto a number line.

all together

Let's investigate

"Think back to your journey here this morning…"

Talk about the things the children saw that had wheels. Ask the same question the next day.

How can we keep a count of all the different things people saw?

Do you think the number of things people saw will be the same or different today? Why do you think that?

"How many children come here on wheels?"

How many do not?

How can we find out?

How can we record our findings?

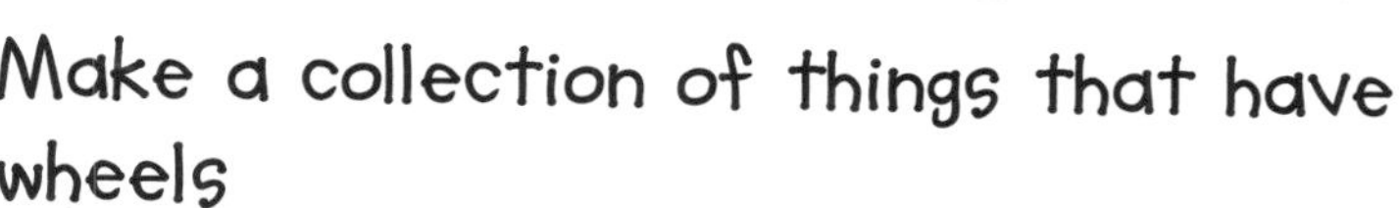

Make a collection of things that have wheels

Include a toy car, a dolls' pram and a wheelbarrow in the collection. Encourage the children to look all around the classroom and to bring things from home.

Are all the wheels the same?

In what ways are the wheels the same/different?

You will need

- dough
- cotton reels, construction kit tyres, wheel-shaped pasta...
- paint and brushes
- paper for printing

how many?
biggest
smallest
shape
flat
curved
round
circle
same
different

Maths learning

Count reliably up to ten everyday objects

Use language to compare two quantities

Use language to describe the shape and size of solids and flat shapes

Roll out

Give the children a circle of thick dough, some pasta wheels, cotton reels and construction kit tyres. Ask them to press the objects into the dough and to paint the top surface of the wheels to make a print base. The children can then put paper on top of the wheel shapes and press to print the designs.

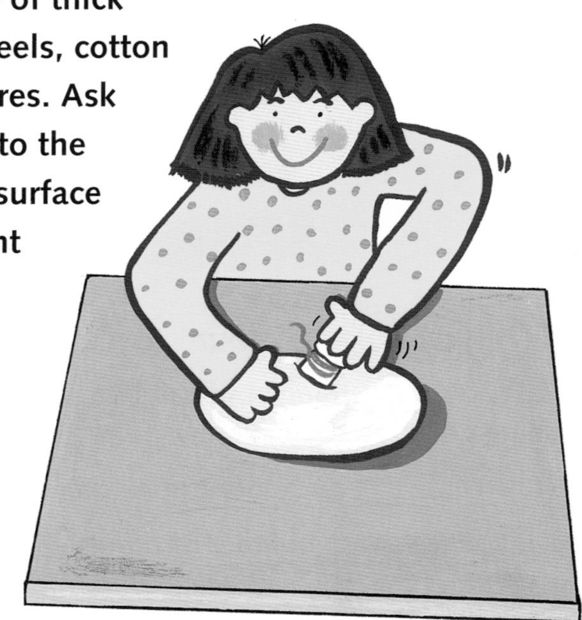

Things to ask

- What did you choose to press into the dough?
- Which objects are the same shape?
- About how many different objects did you use?
- Which is the smallest/biggest object that you pressed?

Challenges

Encourage the children to completely cover the dough circle with wheel shapes.

Ask the children to put their wheel-prints in order of size.

Can the child...

Use mathematical language in play?

Use circles to make a design?

Recognise similarities in circles?

Complete the activity to her satisfaction?

Fishing for wheels

Put different types of wheel in the water tray. Ask the children to take out one sieveful each and then to sort out the wheels they have 'caught'.

Things to ask

- How many wheels did you 'catch'?
- Can you explain how you have sorted them out?
- Which type of wheel did you have the most/fewest of?
- Can you put your sorted collection in order of size?

Challenges

The children use a fishing net to catch one wheel at a time.

Ask the children to decide on a target number and then to catch that number of wheels in a sieve.

Can the child...

Count how many wheels there are in his collection?

Identify which wheel type he has most of?

Use sieves successfully?

Explain his sorted collection?

You will need

- various small wheels, some matching, some different
- a water tray
- sieves or small-handled fishing nets

one, two...
how many?
smallest
largest
most
fewest
order
size
altogether
sort

Maths learning

Count reliably up to ten everyday objects

Use developing mathematical ideas and methods to solve practical problems

Use language to compare two quantities

You will need

- a game board in the shape of a wheel
- small 'people' figures — four per child
- a 1–4 dice

one, two...
first, second...
how many?
last
circle
start from
forwards
finish
how many are left?
what could we try next?

Maths learning

Count reliably up to ten everyday objects

Recognise numerals 1 to 9

Use everyday words to describe position, direction and movement

Spokes to the centre

Give the children a large paper circle with a small circle drawn in the centre and the 'spokes' of a wheel radiating in small squares outwards. The children each have their own spoke and four people figures, and take it in turns to roll the dice. On rolling the dice a child moves one of her people inwards along her spoke for that number of squares. The game continues until all the people are in the centre.

Things to ask

- What number did you roll on the dice?
- Which person are you going to move this time?
- How many people are in the centre of the wheel?
- What will you do if a person is on the square you want to move to?

Challenges

Suggest the children start in the centre and finish on the outside of the wheel.

Children only move a person off the wheel when they roll the exact number.

Can the child...

Recognise numerals to 4?

Count the squares along the spoke accurately?

Think of ways to change the rules of the game?

Keep playing until the game is finished?

Do the rounds

Ask a small group of children to collect 'flat' or 3D objects which could be used as wheels. Next, the children discuss the objects as you put them one by one into a sack. Empty the sack one item at a time and discuss how many different ways we can make each object roll.

Things to ask

- What round things can you see? What are they used for?
- How did you know those things would roll?
- What other round objects could we put in our sack?
- Is it flat and 'circle-shaped' like a CD-ROM , or 'sphere-shaped' like a football?

Challenges

Ask the children to sort the objects that roll in a straight line and objects that roll in different directions.

Give the children washing-up liquid containers to squirt water circles on the outside walls and outside area.

Can the child...

Point out objects that are round?

Find three circular objects?

Use the terms 'circle' and 'sphere' correctly to describe the shapes?

Explore the room and look for shapes independently?

Wheels

You will need

- a wheel
- an assortment of circular and spherical objects
- a sack

compare

the same as

shape

flat

curved

round

sphere

circle

describe

show me

Maths learning

Count reliably up to ten everyday objects

Use developing mathematical ideas and methods to solve practical problems

Use language to describe the shape and size of solids and flat objects

Making tracks

Set up trays of paint to help the children investigate the prints that old wheels can make. Invite the children to roll the wheels, first through the paint and then along sheets of paper on the floor. Afterwards — when the paint is dry — put the prints up on display to discuss together.

You will need

- long trays of paint
- old wheels (from prams, toys, tricycles, construction kits...)
- long sheets of paper (old rolls of wallpaper)

pattern
same
different
wide
narrow
curved
straight
forwards
start (from)
finish

Things to ask

- Did each wheel make a different pattern? Are any tracks the same?
- Can you work out which wheel made which tracks?
- Follow the track of that wheel-print with your finger. Where does it start and where does it finish?
- Can you describe the line made by this wheel? Is it straight or curved?

Challenges

Challenge the children to make circular — or square — track designs using the wheels.

Ask the children to make zigzag track designs. Measure the length of each with a piece of string to find out which track is longest.

Can the child...

Make a wheel print?

Use the language of shape?

Talk clearly about her observations?

Show interest and motivation in this investigation?

Maths learning

Use developing mathematical ideas and methods to solve practical problems

Use language to describe the shape of flat shapes

Use everyday words to describe position, direction and movement

Number wheels

Invite the children to stand in any one of the hoops numbered 1–6, then roll the large dice and call out the number. Ask the children standing in that numbered hoop to collect a wooden numeral of the same number. The children move on to choose other hoops and the game continues until everyone has collected at least one numeral.

Things to ask

- What number does it say on the dice?
- Which children are standing in hoop number four?
- Which numbers have you collected?
- Which number in your collection is the largest?

Challenges

Add numerals 7–10 to the collection. Give the children additional hoops numbered 7–10. Play as before, but hold up cards numbered 1–10 instead of using the dice.

Challenge the children to make a record of the numbers they have collected.

Can the child...

Use some number names?

Recognise numerals up to 6?

Identify the largest number in his collection?

Show involvement in the activity?

Wheels

You will need

- six hoops (numbered 1–6)
- a large 1–6 dice
- 1–6 numerals

number

one, two...

largest

smallest

circle

in

inside

listen

choose

count

Maths learning

Recognise numerals 1 to 9

Use language to compare two numbers

Use everyday words to describe position

Print rollers

Give each of the children a whole, medium-sized potato. With an adult helping, ask the children to carve a design on the potato using a round-ended knife. Next demonstrate how to push a pencil carefully into either side of their carved potato to make 'handles'. Show how to dip a potato print roller into paint to print a border.

You will need

- potatoes
- round-ended knives
- pencils
- paint and tray
- paper for printing
- adults to help

how many?
wide
narrow
pattern
curved
straight
square
rectangle
forwards
describe

Things to ask

- Can you describe your design?
- Have you used any straight or curved lines?
- On your print, where does one roll of the potato start and finish?
- How many rolls of the potato did it take to make your border?

Challenges

The children use the potato roller to print a picture frame on a large piece of paper.

Ask the children to push a pencil through the centre of a cotton reel and wrap some dough around it. They then press a pattern on to the dough and use it with paint as a roller.

Can the child...

Describe her design?

Talk about the shapes she has printed?

Recognise symmetrical patterns?

Show a high level of involvement?

Maths learning

Talk about, recognise and recreate simple patterns

Use language to describe the shape and size of flat shapes

Use everyday words to describe position, direction and movement

Traffic jam

Children work in pairs with the tray of cars in front of them. Each child rolls the dice once, counts out and collects that number of toy cars. They then put their cars together — bumper to bumper — in a line. Give the children some paper, pencils and crayons, and ask them to think of a way of showing the number of cars in their 'traffic jam'. Repeat the activity.

Things to ask

- Which is the longest traffic jam you made? How many cars are in that one?
- Which is the shortest traffic jam you made? How do you know?
- If you add one more car, how many will there be altogether?
- If you take away one car, how many will there be altogether?

Challenges

Ask the children to work out how many cars there are in the traffic jam without counting every car.

The children make a traffic jam and then double the number of cars.

Can the child...

Recognise and name the numbers on the dice?

Select the corresponding number of cars?

Record his work clearly?

Work successfully with a partner?

You will need

- twelve toy cars for each pair
- a tray or box for the cars
- a 1–6 dice
- plain paper
- pencils and crayons

how many?
one more
add
altogether
take away
count (out)
longest
shortest
longer than
shorter than

Maths learning

Count reliably up to ten everyday objects

Begin to use the vocabulary involved in adding and subtracting

Find one more or one less than a number from 1 to 10

Wheels

You will need

- a large collection of toy cars
- a large piece of paper for the 'car park'
- a 1–6 dice
- plain paper
- pencils

one, two...

how many times

full

empty

more

greater

fewer

the same number as

count (out)

Maths learning

Count reliably up to ten everyday objects

Use developing mathematical ideas and methods to solve practical problems

Use language to compare two quantities

Car park

The children take turns to roll the dice and put the corresponding number of cars in the car park. Ask them to record how many dice-rolls it takes until the car park is full. Then empty the car park and start again. Discuss whether it took more or fewer dice-rolls the second time.

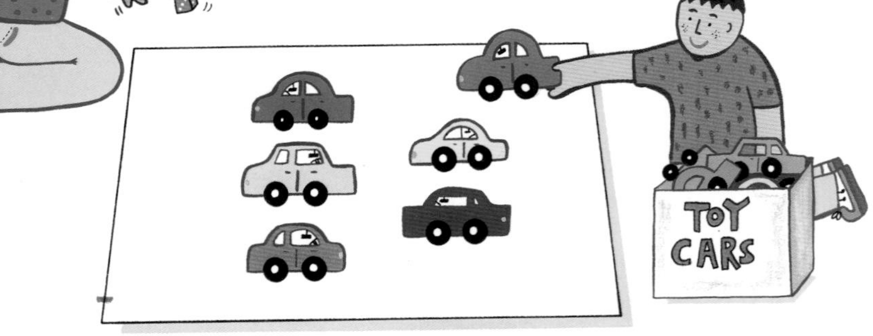

Things to ask

- How many cars are you going to put in the car park this time?
- How many cars are in the car park now?
- Do you have more red cars or white cars in the car park?
- How many dice-rolls did you do altogether?

Challenges

Children roll a numbered and a coloured dice and pick up the corresponding number of cars of that colour. If there is not enough of a particular colour car, no cars can be moved.

The children start the game with the car park full and then empty it by throwing the dice.

Can the child...

Count out a number of cars from the collection?

Accurately record the number of dice rolls?

Compare one result with another to see which is the greater?

Work cooperatively with her partner?

Intercity trains

The children take turns to roll the dice and collect that number of wheels from the box. Each time a child has four wheels he takes a base block to make it into a 'carriage'. The game continues until all the wheels have been used up. Ask the children to join up their carriages and work out whose train is the longest. Then count the carriages and compare numbers.

Things to ask

- What will you do if you roll a three and you only need two wheels on the carriage?
- How can we find out which train is the longest?
- How many carriages are there on your train?
- How many wheels have you got altogether on your train?

Challenges

At the end of the first game, the children play a 'take-off-the-wheels' game.

Give the children a 1–6 dice and ask them to put ten wheels on each carriage.

Can the child...

Count the number of wheels on a carriage?

Count out the wheels from a large collection?

Find the total number of wheels by counting?

Share the wheels when playing the game?

You will need

- a construction kit containing base blocks and attachable wheels
- a tray or box
- a 1–3 dice

number
one, two...
how many?
most
fewest
one more
add
altogether
count (out)
how many are left?
longest

Maths learning

Count reliably up to ten everyday objects

Begin to relate addition to combining two groups of objects

Use language to compare two quantities

Roadway

On a long strip of paper draw a 'roadway' in squares the size of a toy car. Two children lay the roadway on the floor and mark where they want the car to start and where they want it to finish. One child then rolls the dice and gives directions to her partner who moves the car: One clap means 'move forwards'; two claps means 'stop'; three claps means 'move backwards'. Afterwards the children swap roles.

You will need

- a long strip of paper marked in squares
- marker pens
- a toy car
- a 1–3 dice

how many?
one, two...
position
direction
forwards
backwards
listen
start from
finish
what could we try next?

Things to ask

- Why is listening important to this activity?
- How many squares did you move?
- Can you think of other ways to tell your partner to move the car forwards, backwards and to stop?
- What other directions for moving the car could you give your partner?

Challenges

Invite the children to instruct a programmable toy to move along the roadway.

Suggest the children make a roadway with right and left junctions.

Can the child...

Give directions with purpose?

Count the appropriate number of squares?

Think of other ways to give directions?

Listen to and follow directions from another child?

Maths learning

Recognise numerals 1 to 9

Talk about, recognise and recreate simple patterns

Use everyday words to describe position, direction and movement

Bus stop

Arrange ten children in twos to make a 'bus'. The bus then jogs around the hall and stops when it reaches the bus stop. Next roll the dice to find how many children have to get off the bus and sit on the mat. The bus makes three stops in all, and after each turn everyone helps to count how many children got off the bus and how many are left on. Afterwards choose ten other children to make the next bus.

Things to ask

- There are ten children on the bus. Can you count them in twos?
- How many children are on the bus? How many children are on the mat? How many is that altogether?
- There are five children on the bus and five on the mat. If you wrote that as a sum what would it look like? What other way could you write it as a sum?
- How many children got off the bus altogether?

Challenges

Roll two different-coloured 1–3 dice: one shows how many passengers get off the bus; the other shows how many get on the bus.

Use more children to make a bigger bus and roll a 1–6 dice.

Can the child...

Count accurately in ones and twos?

Talk about what is happening to the numbers with understanding?

Suggest a way of recording what happened?

Participate actively as a passenger and a watcher?

You will need

- a large 1–3 dice
- a post or cone to represent a bus stop
- a PE mat
- a whiteboard and marker

one, two...

count in twos

sum

pairs

add

and

make

take away

how many are left?

altogether

Maths learning

Begin to use the vocabulary involved in adding and subtracting

Begin to relate addition to combining two groups of objects

Begin to relate subtraction to 'taking away'

Planning and assessment

The mathematics covered in **Wheels**

Significant steps leading to the Early Learning Goals

	Roll out	Fishing for wheels	Spokes to the centre	Do the rounds	Making tracks	Number wheels	Print rollers	Traffic jam	Car park	Intercity trains	Roadway	Bus stop
Numbers (as labels and for counting)												
use some number names and number language	★	★	★	★		★	★	★	★	★	★	★
count with some numbers in the correct order	★	★	★	★			★	★	★	★	★	★
recognise groups with one, two or three objects	★	★	★	★					★			★
count up to four objects by saying one number name for each	★	★	★	★				★	★	★		★
represent numbers using fingers, pictures or marks on paper								★	★			★
recognise numerals up to 9						★					★	★
count out up to six objects from a larger group		★						★	★	★		★
count up to or beyond ten objects		★		★				★	★	★		★
Numbers (for calculating)												
compare two groups of objects and say when the groups are equal in number								★	★	★		
find the total number of items in two groups by counting all of them									★	★		★
predict how many objects will be left when one or two are taken away								★				★
say the number that is one more than a given number								★				
Shape and space												
use positional language to describe location and movement		★	★	★	★	★	★				★	
select and use shapes appropriately for a given task	★			★	★							
choose to match similar shapes	★	★		★	★							
describe a simple journey					★		★				★	
select an example of a named shape	★			★	★							
show awareness of symmetry	★						★					
find 2D and 3D shapes that will fit together												
Measures												
use measuring language such as 'high', 'short', 'heavy' and words to describe time	★	★		★				★		★		
talk about instruments we can use for measuring, such as hands and scales												
order two or three items by length, height, weight or capacity	★	★		★				★		★		

Shoes

This chapter offers plenty of opportunities for matching. We compare shoes, colourful footprints and socks, and match them into pairs. We describe the different sizes and styles of shoes and sort them into sets. There are counting games, timed shoelace-threading contests, and mathematical activities galore in the shoe shop!

Contents

Shoes

Let's sing

"One, two, buckle my shoe"

Recite this rhyme (stopping at ten or continuing up to twenty) while the children act out the movements.

One, two, buckle my shoe,

Three, four, knock at the door,

Five, six, pick up sticks,

Seven, eight, shut the gate,

Nine, ten, a big fat hen...

Let's do

"Where on your shoe?"

Can you point to the tip of your shoe... the back of your shoe... the side of your shoe... under your shoe.

Which other parts of your shoe can you point to?

One person needs two shoes...

How many shoes would you need for two people? Three people? Four people?

What do you notice about these numbers?

"What is the number on your shoe?"

Why is it there? What does it tell us?

Do we all have the same numbers on our shoes? Why not?

Did your old shoes have the same number as the shoes you are wearing?

all together

Let's investigate

Looking at shoes

The children sit in a circle with legs outstretched.

Look at your own shoes and other people's shoes.

What is the same about the shoes? What is different?

How can we sort ourselves according to our shoes?

"When do you wear shoes?"

Make a chart of when we have our shoes off and when we have them on.

Do you wear shoes in bed? In the bath? In the playground?

What can we find out from the chart?

Toe jam

How many toes are there inside a shoe? In two shoes? Three shoes?

Can you work this out in your head? How can you check your ideas?

Plimsoll line

Discuss how long a line the children could make with their shoes. Ask everyone to take one shoe off and line them all up.

Suppose everybody took off their other shoe to add to the line. How long would the line be then?

You will need

- a pair of shoes
- classroom objects
- two boxes

one, two...
how many?
the same as
count
separate
pair
sort
match
collect
describe
show me

Maths learning

Say and use number names in order in familiar contexts

Count reliably up to ten everyday objects

Use developing mathematical ideas and methods to solve practical problems

Pairs

Show a small group of children a pair of shoes and talk about what a pair is. Ask the children to collect pairs of things such as two bricks, or two books. Separate the pairs into two boxes and ask the children to each take one object from only one of the boxes. Next choose an object from the other box and describe it (without touching it), then wait for the child with the other one of the pair to claim it.

Things to ask

- How many things are there in a pair?
- How many pairs have you collected?
- How did you know I was describing your object?
- How many objects do you think are in the box?

Challenges

Ask the children to help you write labels for all of the pairs.

Suggest the children count how many pairs of objects the group has altogether.

Can the child...

Offer comments about numbers?

Count up to three or four objects reliably?

Make observations about similarities and differences?

Confidently search for objects in different areas of the room?

Whose shoes?

Hold up various shoes, one pair at a time. Ask the children to tell you who the shoes might belong to, and why they think so. Encourage the children to use their imagination, suggesting story characters as well as real-life people. Explain that there can be many different ideas for each pair of shoes.

Things to ask

- Show the children a pair of shoes — such as baby-booties, flippers or wellington boots — and ask, "Who might wear these shoes and what might they be doing?"
- Why do you think these are the giant's shoes?
- Are the shoes you're wearing larger or smaller than this one?
- How many pairs of shoes does the giant need?

Challenges

Mix up the shoes and ask the children to choose one and then to find the other to make a matching pair.

Ask the children to order the shoes from the smallest to the largest.

Can the child...

Make an appropriate choice of shoe for each 'person'?

Explain his reason for deciding who wears a particular shoe?

Decide whether his own shoe is smaller or larger than the one shown?

Feel comfortable and sharing and discussing ideas?

You will need

- different types and sizes of footwear — ask children and parents to help collect these
- big books on giants and babies

how many?
pair
guess
larger
smaller
size
compare
difference between
imagine

Maths learning

Use developing mathematical ideas and methods to solve practical problems

Use language to compare two quantities

Use language to compare the shape and size of solids

Sock washing line

Give the children a collection of socks to sort into matching pairs. Ask them to peg the socks on the line in pairs next to each other.

You will need

- a collection of about ten pairs of socks in different colours and sizes
- a washing line and pegs

how many?
altogether
count
pair
size
sort
match
longer
shorter
the same as
compare

Things to ask

- Which socks are the same?
- Which socks are longer than this pair?
- How many socks are there on the line altogether?
- How many pairs of socks are there altogether?

Challenges

Ask the children to put the pairs of socks on the line in order of size.

Give the children 1–20 number cards to peg one by one in order on the socks.

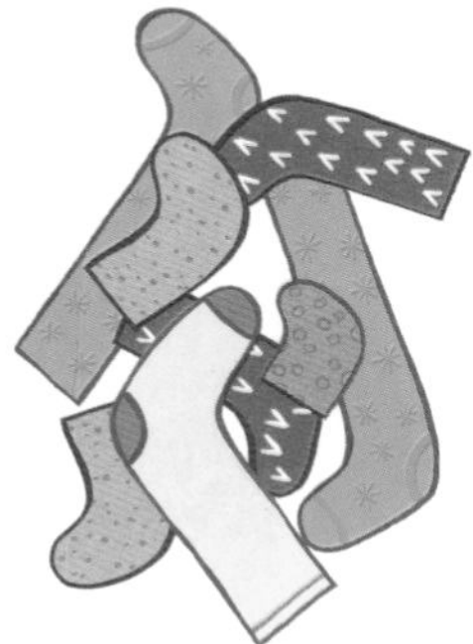

Can the child...

Make observations about the pairs she is choosing?

Begin to count objects one by one?

Use the language of measurement such as 'longer' and 'shorter'?

Cooperate with other children in deciding where the socks are to go on the line?

Maths learning

Count reliably up to ten everyday objects

Use developing mathematical ideas and methods to solve practical problems

Use language to compare two quantities

Match the prints

The children make shoe prints by pressing the soles of their shoes into paint and then onto the paper. Encourage the children to make a print with both the left and the right shoe of a pair. When the prints are dry ask the children to cut out the prints, and together make lines of shoe prints across the room.

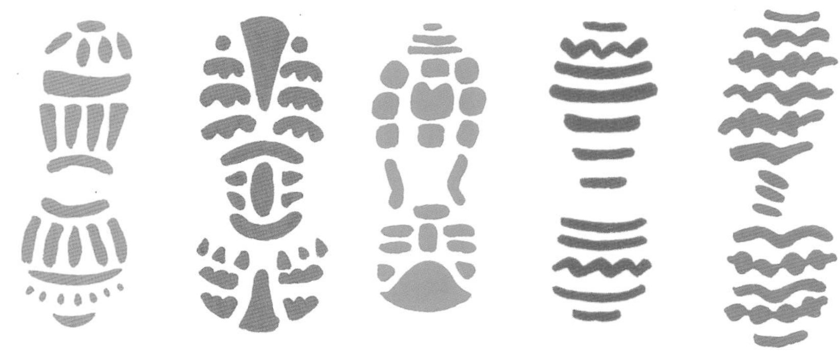

Things to ask

- What different patterns can you see?
- How would you describe this pattern?
- Can you find the shoe that made this pattern?
- How can you check that these two prints match?

Challenges

Using their footprints, the children make a 1–10 number line on a large strip of paper.

Each child prints his footprints on a pair of identical cards. The children put all the cards together and then play Pairs (Pelmanism).

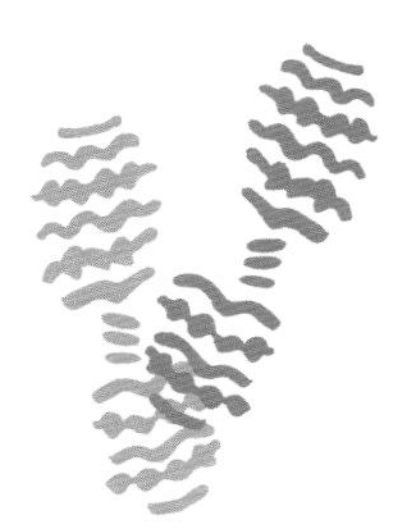

Can the child...

Describe the patterns made in his own words?

Find a matching pair of prints?

Find the shoe that made the print?

Work cooperatively in a group situation?

You will need

- old shoes with different patterned soles
- paint
- large sheets of paper

pattern
the same as
match
pair
size
left
right
curved
straight
look at
describe

Maths learning

Talk about, recognise and recreate simple patterns

Use developing mathematical ideas and methods to solve practical problems

Use language to compare two quantities

Find the footprints

You will need

- lots of footprints cut from black sugar paper or card
- a clip-board for each child in the group

how many?
one, two...
more
fewer
most
fewest
under
above
on
position
across
along

Before school begins stick up sets of footprints in different places around the room — up a door, across a window, along a table top... Send a small group of 'detectives' off to locate the footsteps in each place and count them.

Things to ask

- Where did you find the most footprints?
- Where did you find the fewest footprints?
- Were there more footprints across the window or on the table?
- How many footprints did you find?

Challenges

The children record how many footprints they found in each place. Supply cut-outs of small footprints and a marked-up sheet of paper with squares the size of the footprints.

Can the children make a trail of footprints leading to some treasure?

Maths learning

Count reliably up to ten everyday objects

Use language to compare two quantities

Use everyday words to describe position

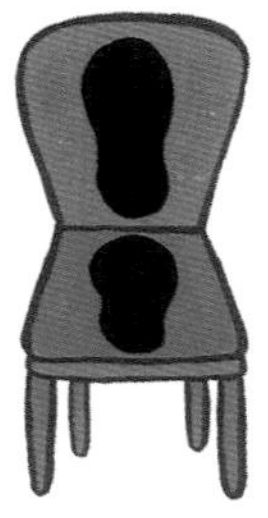

Can the child...

Describe the position of the footprints in her own way?

Use number names to describe her counting?

Compare two numbers and say which is more?

Show an interest in the search for footprints?

Shoe filling

Ask the children to use the collection of shoes to fill in the shapes drawn on the large pieces of paper. Invite other children to guess how many shoes were used to fill in the shapes. When all the children have had a guess, count the shoes in each shape and discuss the results.

Things to ask

- Just look; don't count. Do you think Shirley's shape has more than five shoes, or fewer than five shoes?
- How did you know that there were five shoes in this shape without counting them one by one?
- What is it about this shape that makes it easy to guess the number of shoes?
- Which shape has the most shoes inside?

Challenges

Ask the children to take a photograph of each shape and its shoes to make a 'guess and count' book.

Invite the children to rearrange the shoes into another shape and draw the outline.

Can the child...

Fill a shape with the shoes?

Look at the shoes and suggest how many there are?

Count how many shoes there are in a shape?

Work cooperatively with other children?

You will need

- a large collection of shoes
- large shapes drawn on large pieces of paper

more
guess
fewer
most
fewest
shape
circle
triangle
square
rectangle
inside

Maths learning

Use language to compare two numbers

Use language to compare two quantities

Use everyday words to describe position

You will need

- a copy of the rhyme 'There Was An Old Woman...'
- a shoe for each child
- a box of play people

inside
guess
how many?
more
less
fewer
one less
one more
too many
not enough
the same number

Maths learning

Count reliably up to ten everyday objects

Use developing mathematical ideas and methods to solve practical problems

Use language to compare two quantities

Living in a shoe

Together discuss the rhyme 'There Was An Old Woman Who Lived In A Shoe'. Then ask the children to find out how many play people they can fit in a shoe.

Things to ask

- How many do you think will fit in this shoe?
- Will this shoe hold more or less?
- What's the best way to count how many are in the shoe?
- Could the same number of elephants live in the shoe?

Challenges

The children make a display of the shoes and the number of occupants they have.

Can the children find a shoe that ten dinosaurs could live in. Can they find one for ten mice?

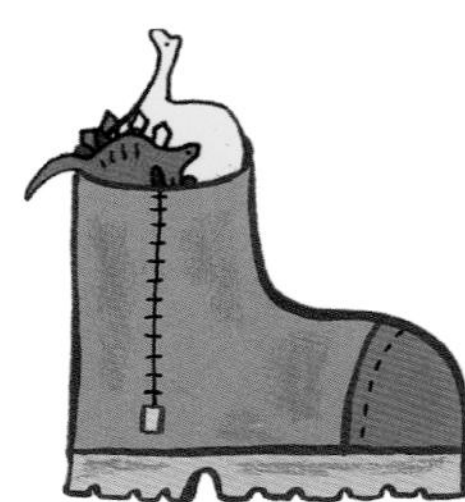

Can the child...

Give a realistic estimate of objects that might fit?

Put three shoes in order of capacity?

Show an understanding of 'more' and 'less' in this context?

Show a high level of involvement?

Shoe boxes

Attach a different number card to each box and ask the children to put the right number of objects inside each one.

Things to ask

- Can you say the number on each box?
- How many objects are there in that box?
- Can you put the boxes in order from the smallest to the largest number?
- How can you check that you have the right number of objects?

Challenges

Take the number cards off the boxes and move the boxes to different positions. Ask the children to work out which number card goes on which box.

Ask the children if they need to put, for example, 'more than five', or 'fewer than seven' objects into a box.

Can the child...

Recognise the numerals and name them?

Count accurately, check and self-correct?

Match a numeral to a number of objects?

Complete the activity to his satisfaction?

You will need

- empty boxes
- a set of 0–10 number cards
- sticky tape
- a large collection of small objects

how many?
one, two...
number
count
more
fewer
largest
smallest
order
check

Maths learning

Say and use number names in order in familiar contexts

Count reliably up to ten everyday objects

Recognise numerals 1 to 9

Shoes

You will need

- large 1–6 number cards (for the challenge)

count
number
one, two...
how many?
too many
too few
behind
forwards
largest
smallest
start from
explain

Maths learning

Say and use number names in order in familiar contexts

Use language to compare two numbers

Use everyday words to describe position, direction and movement

Grandma's footsteps

In this old playground game one person is 'Grandma' and everyone else stands some distance away behind her. The children then ask, "How many steps Grandma?" Grandma calls out a number and the children take that many steps towards her. She turns round occasionally, and anyone she sees moving is sent back to the start. The aim is to reach Grandma without being seen.

Things to ask

- Can you explain how you play the game?
- How many steps do you think it would take to reach Grandma?
- Does it make a difference if you take small or big steps?
- What was the largest number Grandma called out?

Challenges

Grandma holds up a number card above her head for the children to see. The children move that number of steps.

Grandma describes the numbers she is thinking of: "This number is one more than five", or "This is the number that comes before four".

Can the child...

Join in using number language?

Count as she makes footsteps?

Estimate how many more steps are needed to reach Grandma?

Understand how to play the game?

Lace them up

Give each child a shoe shape and lace, and together practise threading the laces in and out through the holes. Then set the sand timer and ask the children to thread the laces through as many holes as they can before the sand runs out in a minute's time. Discuss and compare the results.

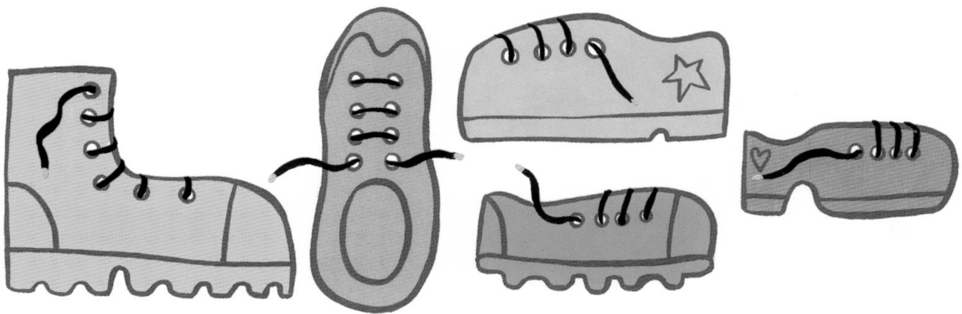

Things to ask

- How many holes did you thread in one minute?
- How many holes do you think you could thread in two minutes?
- How many more holes do you need to thread to make eight holes altogether?
- How could we find out how many holes were threaded altogether?

Challenges

With the help of an adult, children make their own shoe shapes, punch holes through, and thread laces.

Children use a variety of ribbons and laces and weave them through dishcloth fabric to make a collage.

Can the child...

Count the number of holes threaded?

Count how many more holes are needed to reach a certain number?

Work out how to double the number?

Successfully thread a lace through the holes?

You will need

- shoe shapes punched with holes
- one lace per shoe
- a one-minute sand timer

how many?
altogether
count
guess
more
minute
over
under
in
out

Maths learning

Count reliably up to ten everyday objects

Use developing mathematical ideas and methods to solve practical problems

Use everyday words to describe position, direction and movement

Shoes

You will need

- shoes
- shoe boxes
- a calculator
- a till and money
- Post-It notes or paper and sticky tape

one two...
larger
smaller
pound
pence
size
longer
shorter
wider
narrower
left
right

Maths learning

Recognise numerals 1 to 9

Use language to compare two numbers

Find one more or one less than a number from 1 to 10

Shoe shop

Turn the role-play area into a shoe shop with shoes, shoe boxes, and so on. Include some Post-It notes or paper and sticky tape. Ask a few children to price the shoes and find out what size each one is. Then encourage the 'customers' to ask for a particular size when they go to the shoe shop. The shopkeeper looks to see if it is in stock.

Things to ask

- Who do you think would wear this shoe?
- Is your shoe larger or smaller than this one?
- Are these shoes the same size as those? How are they different?
- How could you find out what size shoes you wear?

Challenges

Ask a group of children to keep a shoe stock-control list.

Have a sale and ask the children to reduce the price of all the shoes.

Can the child...

Order two or three items by length?

Use number names accurately in play?

Read and use the information on the labels with understanding?

Talk about what she is doing?

Do up your shoes

Discuss the children's various types of shoe fastenings. Lay two hoops on the ground. Ask a child wearing lace-ups to put one of his shoes in the 'with laces' hoop, and a child who isn't to put his shoe in the 'without laces' hoop. Invite the remaining children to do the same. Afterwards compare the two groups.

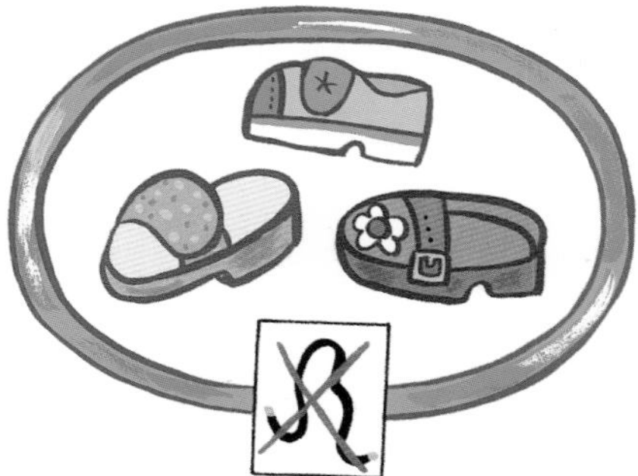

Things to ask

- Which hoop has the most shoes in it? How many shoes are there in it?
- What sort of fastenings do all these shoes have?
- Which hoop has the fewest shoes? How many shoes are in it?
- How many more children are wearing shoes with laces than shoes with buckles today?

Challenges

Ask each child to line up behind the person wearing the same type of shoe as himself. Ask the children to point out which line is the longest.

Challenge the children to think of another way to sort the shoes.

Can the child...

Count an irregular arrangement of up to ten objects?

Find the total number of shoes in two groups by counting?

Know how many shoes will be left when one or two are taken away?

Talk about which group his shoes belong to and why?

You will need

- children with their shoes on
- two hoops
- card for labels

one, two...
altogether
add
take away
how many more?
more
most
fewest
sort
set
in
the same as

Maths learning

Begin to use the vocabulary involved in adding and subtracting

Begin to relate addition to combining two groups of objects

Use language to compare two quantities

Planning and assessment

The mathematics
covered in **Shoes**

Significant steps leading to the Early Learning Goals

	Pairs	Whose shoes?	Sock washing line	Match the prints	Find the footprints	Shoe filling	Living in a shoe	Shoe boxes	Grandma's footsteps	Lace them up	Shoe shop	Do up your shoes
Numbers (as labels and for counting)												
use some number names and number language	★		★		★	★	★	★	★	★	★	★
count with some numbers in the correct order	★		★		★	★	★	★	★	★		★
recognise groups with one, two or three objects	★	★	★	★		★		★				★
count up to four objects by saying one number name for each	★		★		★	★	★	★	★	★		★
represent numbers using fingers, pictures or marks on paper											★	
recognise numerals up to 9								★			★	
count out up to six objects from a larger group										★		
count up to or beyond ten objects	★		★		★	★	★	★		★		★
Numbers (for calculating)												
compare two groups of objects and say when the groups are equal in number					★	★	★					★
find the total number of items in two groups by counting all of them										★		★
predict how many objects will be left when one or two are taken away												★
say the number that is one more than a given number											★	
Shape and space												
use positional language to describe location and movement				★	★	★	★		★	★		★
select and use shapes appropriately for a given task		★										
choose to match similar shapes	★	★	★	★								★
describe a simple journey									★			
select an example of a named shape	★					★						
show awareness of symmetry				★								
find 2D and 3D shapes that will fit together												
Measures												
use measuring language such as 'high', 'short', 'heavy' and words to describe time		★	★					★	★	★	★	
talk about instruments we can use for measuring, such as hands and scales										★		
order two or three items by length, height, weight or capacity		★	★				★	★			★	

Sand

This chapter encourages us to read and draw numerals. Dice and number cards tell us how many cupfuls of sand to count out, how many straws to take, or which flag to collect. We dig in sand to find a specific number of objects — and we use subtraction to work out how many objects are still buried. We think of words for shape and size, and use them to describe, compare and sort the objects we have found. And, of course, we find time to make sandcastles and race against the sand timer!

Contents

Sand

Let's sing

The sand hopper song

All do the actions to go with the song.

This little sand hopper broke his toe, **(hold up thumb)**

This little sand hopper said, "oh, oh!" **(hold up first finger)**

This little sand hopper laughed and was glad, **(hold up middle finger)**

This little sand hopper cried and was sad. **(hold up third finger)**

This little sand hopper, thoughtful and good, **(hold up little finger)**

Ran for the doctor as fast as she could. **(make fingers run)**

Let's do

"How much sand can you hold in your hand?"

How much do you think? About a cupful? A tubful?

How can you find out?

How much sand can you hold in two hands?

"Let's sort the sand play toys"

Sort the sand play toys according to what the children can do with them.

Which toys can we pour sand through?

Which toys can we fill with sand?

How else might we sort them?

all together

Let's investigate

Sand weights

Measure identical amounts of dry sand into two separate containers. Add water to one and ask the children to predict which they think will be heavier.

Why did you choose that one?

How can we check if it is heavier?

Drying out

Put a pile of wet sand in a tray and ask the children to guess how long they think it will take to dry.

What can we do to find out if it is dry yet?

How can we measure how long it takes?

Wet and dry

Discuss all the words we can use to describe dry sand or wet sand. Together, make a chart with two columns and add to it during the week (ask parents to help). At the end of the week count up the number of words collected.

What other words can you think of?

Which column has more words: the list for dry sand or the list for wet sand?

"How long does it take to tidy the sand tray?"

Use a one-minute sand timer to find out how long it takes to tidy the sand tray (or home corner). Record the result each day. At the end of the week, invite the quickest tidiers to share their tips.

Do you think anyone can beat that record next week?

Sand

You will need

- pencils
- pieces of card the size of a hand
- glue and glue stick/brush
- sand

number
zero
one, two...
curved
straight
around
up
down
across
write
trace
copy

Maths learning

Recognise numerals 1 to 9

Find one more or one less than a number from 1 to 10

Use everyday words to describe position, direction and movement

Sandy numbers

Show the children how to make 'sandy numbers'. Write a number on a piece of card, paint over it with glue and carefully sprinkle sand all over. Shake off the excess sand to reveal the sandy number. Ask the children to make their own sandy numbers.

Things to ask

- **Which numbers have you made? What are you going to make next?**
- **How can you tell which numbers you still need to make?**
- **Which numbers have straight lines? Which numbers have curved lines? Which numbers have both?**
- **Can you show me the number that comes after four?**

Challenges

Use a set of numbers made from sandpaper for a 'feely' number activity. A child closes her eyes, feels the number and tries to identify it.

Ask the children to close their eyes and then put the numbers in order. Ask how they will do this.

Can the child...

Form the numerals correctly?

Name the numeral she has made?

Identify and correct a numeral that is the wrong way round?

Work in an organised manner?

Hidden numbers

Hide some plastic or wooden numerals in the sand tray. Ask the children to see how many they can find before the one-minute sand timer runs out.

Things to ask

- What is this number called?
- Which numbers have straight lines? Which numbers have curved lines? Which numbers have both?
- Did you find any numbers that were the same?
- How many numbers did you find?

Challenges

Ask the children to make a record of numbers that they found.

The children close their eyes and try to form a recognisable numeral in the sand.

Can the child...

Put the number the right way round?

Name the numbers he found?

Recognise and discuss the similarities in shape between certain numerals?

Work cooperatively in a group?

You will need

- a sand tray
- a sand timer
- wooden or plastic 0–9 numerals

number

zero

one, two...

how many?

the same

curved

straight

turn

find

collect

different

same

Maths learning

Count reliably up to ten everyday objects

Recognise numerals 1 to 9

Use language to describe the shape of flat shapes

You will need

- a 1–3 dice
- a tray of damp sand
- sixteen or more 'fence posts' (such as lolly sticks)
- four farm animals

one, two...
one more...
how many?
how many are left?
nearly
enough
add
makes
altogether
square

Maths learning

Count reliably up to ten everyday objects

Begin to use the vocabulary involved in adding and subtracting

Use language to describe the shape and size of flat shapes

Fences

The children work in pairs, taking turns. The first child rolls the dice and picks up that number of 'fence posts'. When she has collected four posts, she makes up an enclosure in the damp sand and puts a farm animal inside. She continues to roll the dice and collect posts until all the animals are in enclosures. It is then her partner's turn to roll the dice.

Things to ask

- How many fence posts have you collected?
- What shape will you make your enclosure?
- How many more fence posts do you need?
- Can you explain how to play the game?

Challenges

Use a 1–6 dice and make enclosures with ten fence posts.

Suggest the children play the game in reverse, taking down fence posts as they roll that number on the dice.

Can the child...

Recognise dice patterns?

Collect the appropriate fence posts?

Recognise when she has enough posts to make an enclosure?

Take turns in rolling the dice?

Give away potfuls

Children work in pairs. Each child has the same-sized yoghurt pot and a half-bucketful of sand. They take turns to roll a dice. If the dice shows one spot they put one potful of their sand into the other child's container; if it shows two spots they put in two potfuls, and so on. The game ends when one player has given away all of his sand.

Things to ask

- What number does the dice show? So what must you do?
- How did you feel when you had to give your sand away?
- Compare Ian's sand with Jordan's. Can you guess who has less sand?
- Can you make up your own game with the pots and sand?

Challenges

Use a 1–6 dice and smaller yoghurt pots.

Have only five dice rolls each and then find out who has the most sand.

Can the child...

Recognise the number of dots on the dice?

Estimate who has less sand?

Invent another game?

Cooperate with the other player throughout the game?

You will need

- pairs of identical yoghurt pots
- pairs of identical buckets
- dry sand
- a 1–3 dice with 'miss a go'

one, two...
the same as
more than
less than
most
least
compare
one more
heaviest
lightest

Maths learning

Begin to use the vocabulary involved in adding and subtracting

Use developing mathematical ideas and methods to solve practical problems

Use language to compare two quantities

Sand

You will need

- a sand tray
- a collection of shells to hide in the sand
- buckets
- sieves

more
fewer
bigger
smaller
most
fewest
empty
collect
explain
work out
same
different

Maths learning

Count reliably up to ten everyday objects

Use developing mathematical ideas and methods to solve practical problems

Use language to compare two quantities

Sieve it out

Explain that someone has hidden lots of shells in the sand tray. Children work in pairs and each collects a bucketful of the sand and shell mix. Next ask each child to sieve the mixture in her bucket and to hold on to the shells. Discuss which bucket contains more shells.

Things to ask

- How will you know when you have found all the shells?
- Why won't the shells go through the holes in the sieve?
- How can we find out which bucket has more shells?
- How can you make sure you don't count the same shell twice?

Challenges

Challenge the children to count how many shells there are in each sieve.

The children try to make the number of shells in both buckets the same.

Can the child...

Think of a way to identify which bucket has more shells?

Talk about the differences between quantities of shells in the two buckets?

Discuss the difference in size between the holes in the sieve and the shells?

Carry out the task independently with understanding?

Sandcastle straws

Place a newly made sandcastle in the middle of the table. Ask the children to take turns to stick lots of coloured straws into it without letting it collapse. Next the children take turns to roll the dice and take out a straw of that colour from the sandcastle. If there are no straws of that colour left, the player may roll the dice just once more. When all the straws have gone, players find out who has the most straws.

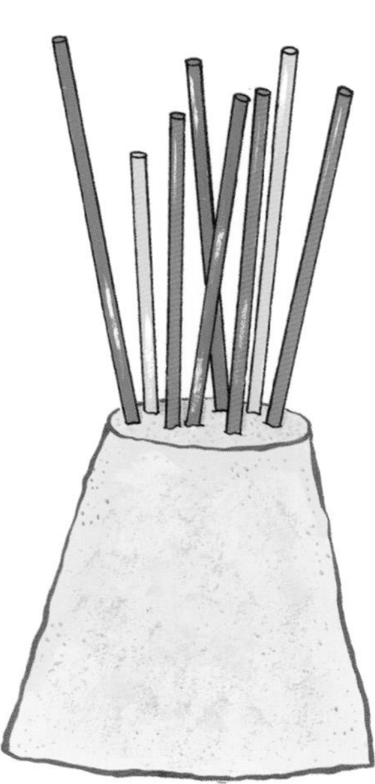

Things to ask

- How many red straws have you each got?
- Who has the most yellow straws?
- Who has the most straws altogether?
- How could you change this game? What other things could you stick in the sand? What different type of dice would you need to make?

Challenges

When all the straws have been taken, a child rolls the dice once more to find the winning colour. Whoever has the most straws in that colour wins.

Challenge the children to make a record of how many straws in each colour were collected.

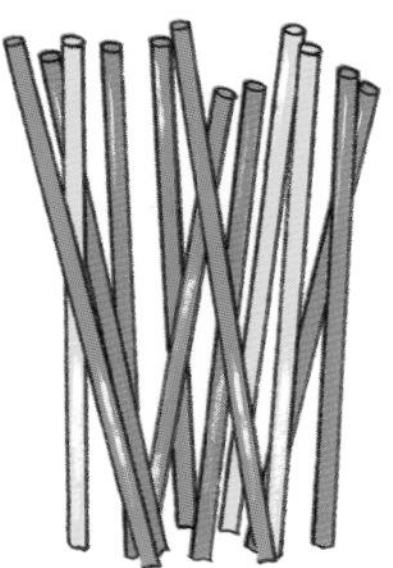

Can the child...

Select the appropriate colour of straw?

Count his straws?

Compare the number of his straws with other players'?

Think of an appropriate variation to the game and explain how to play it?

You will need

- sand
- a bucket or mould
- red, green and yellow straws
- a dice with two red, two green and two yellow faces

how many?
count
altogether
more
fewer
most
fewest
the same as
take away
how many are left?

Maths learning

Count reliably up to ten everyday objects

Begin to use the vocabulary involved in adding and subtracting

Use language to compare two quantities

Sand

Sand writing

Help the children to make cones from the card. Then ask them to fill their cones with dry sand using the spade or container. Encourage the children to write some numerals with the trailing sand on the black paper.

You will need

- sand
- small spades/ containers
- thin card to make funnel
- large sheets of black paper

number
zero
one, two...
curved
straight
up
down
around
across
start from
describe

Things to ask

- Can you make some numbers that have straight lines and some that have curved lines?
- Which numbers have you made? Which number are you going to make next?
- Can you describe how you made that number?
- Can you write the number that comes after six?

Challenges

Ask the children to form numerals 1–9 in order.

Challenge a child with her eyes closed to guess — by listening to the description — which sand number her partner is writing.

Can the child...

Form the numerals correctly?

Recognise similarities between the shapes of numerals ?

Explain with confidence how the numerals are formed?

Remain focused on the activity?

Maths learning

Recognise numerals 1 to 9

Find one more or one less than a number from 1 to10

Use everyday words to describe position, direction and movement

Hide the treasure

Ask one child to bury an object of his choice in the sand so that only a small part is showing. Ask another child to guess what the object is, then to dig it up to check. Let the children explore lots of objects in this way: natural things such as acorns and fir cones; mathematics equipment such as 3D shapes and wooden numerals; and toys such as animals and cars.

Things to ask

- You think that it's a car. Which parts of the car can you see above the sand? Which parts do you think are below?
- You think it's a lion. Is more of the lion above or below the sand? How do you know?
- Why does Maisy think this could be either a spoon, a fork or a knife? What does she need to see before she can tell which one it is?
- Can you describe one of the objects sticking out above the sand?

Challenges

Bury metallic objects completely in the sand and challenge the children to hunt for them with magnets.

One group of children makes an island in the sand, buries some treasure and draws a map to show the other children where to look.

Can the child...

Make a guess based on observation?

Compare his guess to the actual results?

Describe how much of the object is above/below the sand?

Show understanding of the task?

You will need

- a tray of dry sand
- objects to bury

more
less
guess
under
above
below
check
look at
describe
part
whole

Maths learning

Use developing mathematical ideas and methods to solve practical problems

Use language to compare two quantities

Use everyday words to describe position

Sand

You will need

- a tray of dry sand
- objects to bury
- 1–9 number cards

number

one, two...

how many?

count

more

match

find

work out

check

how many are left?

Maths learning

Count reliably up to ten everyday objects

Recognise numerals 1 to 9

Use developing mathematical ideas and methods to solve practical problems

Lucky dip

Before the session bury some objects in the sand and either display a number card showing how many are hidden or — for younger children — make a 'matching' card by drawing around the items before hiding them. Ask a pair of children to try and find them all.

Things to ask

- How many objects are hidden? How do you know that?
- You've found three things. How many are still hidden? How do you know?
- How will you know when you have found all the hidden objects?
- Which object goes on this outline?

Challenges

One pair of children discusses objects to hide in a 'lucky dip' for another pair. They count the objects, record the number and then bury them in the sand tray.

Collect pairs of objects and hide one of each pair — plus an extra object — in the sand tray. Display the remaining objects nearby. Challenge the children to dig up the objects to find the odd one out!

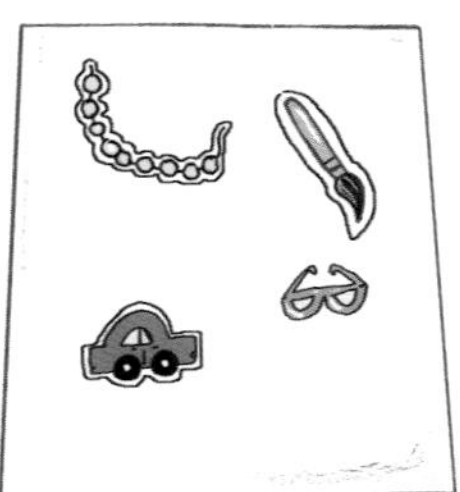

Can the child...

Keep count of the objects as she finds them?

Work out how many more objects she needs to find?

Recognise when all the objects have been found?

Cooperate with her partner?

Flags

Make six sandcastles. With the children's help make a few flags for each, using the card, lolly sticks and sticky tape. Put spots on the flags — ranging from one to six — so that each flag matches a different dice number.

Ask the children to put the flags on the sandcastles. The children then take turns to roll the dice and collect a flag showing the same number of spots. The game continues until all the flags have been collected.

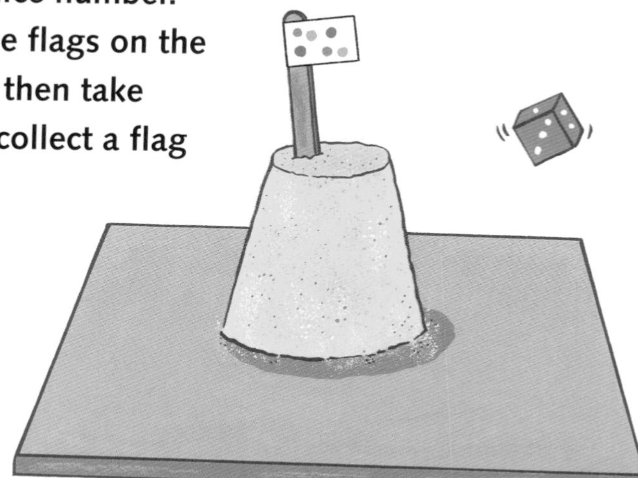

Things to ask

- Which spotty flag do you need to collect?
- Can you show me which dice this flag matches?
- How many three-spot flags did you collect?
- How many different flags did you collect?

Challenges

Supply a few sets of 1–6 spotty flags and challenge the children to collect a complete set each. Ask them to put their set in order to finish.

Give the children a 1–10 spinner and 1–10 spotty flags.

Can the child...

Recognise the dot patterns on the dice?

Match the number of dots on the dice and flags?

Think of a way of arranging his collection?

Understand the idea of taking turns in a game?

You will need

- sand
- a bucket or mould
- card
- crayons
- lolly sticks
- sticky tape
- a 1–6 dice

number
how many?
one, two...
count
pattern
compare
match
the same as
show me
collect

Maths learning

Count reliably up to ten everyday objects

Talk about, recognise and recreate simple patterns

Use developing mathematical ideas and methods to solve practical problems

Sand

You will need

- a tray of dry sand
- ten cubes per pair
- two sets of wooden 1–5 numerals per pair

how many?
altogether
count out
make
enough
add
check
explain

Finding how many

Ask the children to work in pairs and bury lots of cubes in the sand tray. Each child then takes a wooden numeral from the bag and digs up that number of cubes. Both children then put their cube collections together and work out how many they have altogether.

Things to ask

- The numeral says 5. How many cubes must you dig up?
- How do you know if you have dug up enough cubes? How can you check?
- How many cubes have you and your partner dug up altogether? How can you work it out?
- Can you explain how you counted your cubes?

Challenges

Two children each pick up a wooden 1–5 numeral and hide that number of cubes in the sand. Ask the group how many cubes are hidden altogether.

Hide ten cubes in the sand. Ask a child to take a numeral from the bag and collect that number of cubes. Challenge her to work out how many cubes are left in the sand.

Maths learning

Begin to use the vocabulary involved in adding and subtracting

Begin to relate addition to combining two groups of objects

Use developing mathematical ideas and methods to solve practical problems

Can the child...

Count the cubes she has dug up?

Explain how to count her cube findings?

Find a reliable method to work out and check her answers?

Work cooperatively with a partner?

What's it worth?

Hide a selection of beads in the sand. Explain to the children that yellow beads are worth two pennies and red beads are worth one penny. Working in pairs, the children have to find as many beads as they can, exchange them for pennies and work out how much their collection is worth.

Things to ask

- How many yellow beads did you find, and how many red beads?
- What are your beads worth altogether?
- Can you explain how you worked out your total?
- Whose beads are worth the most? How do you know?

Challenges

Challenge children to collect beads to a specific value: "Can you make a collection of beads that is worth eight pennies?"

Add green beads, worth five pennies each, to the game.

Can the child...

Exchange his beads for the correct number of pennies?

Count a set of 1p coins accurately?

Work out how much his beads are worth altogether?

Take an active part in the activity?

You will need

- a tray of dry sand
- red and yellow beads
- pencils and paper
- a large collection of pennies

count (up)
altogether
makes
add
most
coin
penny
worth
how much?
work out
exchange

Maths learning

Count reliably up to ten everyday objects

Use developing mathematical ideas and methods to solve practical problems

Use language to compare two quantities

Planning and assessment

The mathematics covered in **Sand**

Significant steps leading to the Early Learning Goals

	Sandy numbers	Hidden numbers	Fences	Give away potfuls	Sieve it out	Sandcastle straws	Sand writing	Hide the treasure	Lucky dip	Flags	Finding how many	What's it worth?
Numbers (as labels and for counting)												
use some number names and number language	★	★	★	★	★	★	★		★	★	★	★
count with some numbers in the correct order	★	★	★	★	★	★			★	★	★	★
recognise groups with one, two or three objects			★			★				★		
count up to four objects by saying one number name for each		★	★	★	★	★				★	★	★
represent numbers using fingers, pictures or marks on paper	★						★					
recognise numerals up to 9	★	★					★		★		★	
count out up to six objects from a larger group			★						★		★	★
count up to or beyond ten objects		★			★				★	★	★	★
Numbers (for calculating)												
compare two groups of objects and say when the groups are equal in number			★		★	★			★			
find the total number of items in two groups by counting all of them			★								★	
predict how many objects will be left when one or two are taken away						★						
say the number that is one more than a given number	★						★					
Shape and space												
use positional language to describe location and movement	★						★	★				
select and use shapes appropriately for a given task			★									
choose to match similar shapes		★	★									
describe a simple journey												
select an example of a named shape												
show awareness of symmetry								★				
find 2D and 3D shapes that will fit together												
Measures												
use measuring language such as 'high', 'short', 'heavy' and words to describe time				★	★			★				
talk about instruments we can use for measuring, such as hands and scales												
order two or three items by length, height, weight or capacity				★								

Bodies

There's so much mathematics we can do with our bodies both indoors and out. From measuring ourselves with ribbons to stretching our bodies into different shapes, there's plenty of scope for active learning! We count our own actions, form groups to create an 'action number line' and think of ways of recording results. We read numerals, create numbers, and have fun looking for a partner whose dots card can be added to ours to make a certain number.

Contents

Bodies

Let's sing

"Head, shoulders, knees and toes"

Sing the rhyme and encourage the children to join in with the actions.

Head, shoulders, knees and toes, knees and toes,

Head, shoulders, knees and toes, knees and toes,

And eyes and ears and mouth and nose,

Head, shoulders, knees and toes, knees and toes.

Let's do

"Stand up, sit down"

Everyone sits on the carpet, counts out loud to ten and shouts, "Stand up, sit down!" Each child then quickly decides which action to do. Choose five children to estimate how many people are standing and how many are sitting, then everybody counts to find out the answer.

"Let's all stand in a line and hold hands with our arms outstretched..."

How far will our line reach?

Let's investigate

"Where have you been today?"

Make a large map of the room and outdoor play area, and cover it in sticky backed plastic. Before home time, ask the children to think about all the different parts of the room and outdoor area they have visited today. Invite one child at a time to record where he has been by putting sticky dots on the map.

Have you been at the sand tray, in the brick area, or in the home corner?

Have you been in every part of the room this morning?

Have you been outdoors today?

What does the map show?

"How long is a minute?"

Ask the children to sit as still as they can for one minute, to watch all the sand run through the timer. Next take the children out to the playground and let them play for one whole minute.

Did that feel like a long time or a short time?

Did playing feel like a longer time or a shorter time than sitting down to watch the timer?

When else does time seem to be going slowly?

Why does a minute feel different sometimes?

Bodies

You will need

- drawing materials or a camera (for the challenge)

number

count

how many?

same

group

decide

order

before

after

start with

number line

What are they doing?

Children take it in turns to act out an activity such as digging, running or drawing while everybody else tries to guess what they are doing. Ask the children to make an action number line together: one child jumping, two children clapping, three children hopping and so on.

Things to ask

- How many children do we need next to join the line?
- What could four children be doing? Any ideas?
- How many children are jumping/hopping/clapping?
- How did your group decide which action you would do together?

Challenges

The children record the bodies action line by drawing or taking photographs.

Ask the children to invent a new version of the song 'Peter Hammers With One Hammer'.

Can the child...

Talk about or show an interest in numbers?

Use some number names?

Count actions?

Willingly join in with the activity?

Maths learning

Say and use number names in order in familiar contexts

Count reliably up to ten everyday objects

Talk about, recognise and recreate simple patterns

How we've changed

Ask the children to match photographs of themselves as babies with recent photographs. Discuss the changes. Make a simple 'flap' book or poster, with a baby photo of each child on the lift-up flaps and the present-day pictures underneath.

Things to ask

- Which baby photo do you think is Sammy's?
- What clues did you find?
- Which of Karl's photos was taken a long time ago? Which one was taken just a short time ago?
- About how old do you think Nina is in this picture? Why do you think that?

Challenges

Ask the children to sort the photos into sets and explain why they have sorted them that way.

Find out who is the oldest/youngest. Ask the children to help you make a birthday washing line, with the months of the year and a photo of each child.

Can the child...

Show understanding of the tasks?

Match the photos together?

Begin to use time words?

Explain what he has done?

You will need

- photographs of the children as babies and as they are now
- thin card or sugar paper
- felt-tipped pens
- Blu-Tack

match

remember

now

then

older

younger

how old?

this year

how long ago?

long time ago

short time ago

Maths learning

Say and use number names in order in familiar contexts

Use developing mathematical ideas and methods to solve practical problems

Use language to compare two quantities

Getting dressed

Ask the children to think about getting dressed to come to school. What do they put on first/second/third/last of all? Explain that the teddies also need to put their clothes on in the correct order. To play Dress The Teddies, children take turns to roll the dice and put the item of clothing showing on their bear. Finish when the first teddy is fully dressed.

You will need

- a teddy for each child
- teddy-sized pants, vests, trousers, T-shirts, hats and scarves
- a dice showing the above clothing

order
first
second
third
last
before
after
next
over

Things to ask

- Does everyone put the same things on first?
- What would happen if you put your shoes on before your socks?
- Can you explain how to play the game?
- What will you do if your teddy is already wearing a scarf?

Challenges

Use a 1–6 dice: roll a one for pants; ...two for a vest; ...three for trousers; ...four for a T-shirt; ...five for a hat; ...six for a scarf.

Have a race to see who can dress their teddy in the correct order the fastest.

Maths learning

Say and use number names in order in familiar contexts

Talk about, recognise and recreate simple patterns

Use developing mathematical ideas and methods to solve practical problems

Can the child...

Suggest solutions to problems?

Tell you the order in which she gets dressed?

Use ordinal words such as first, second, last?

Make decisions when playing the game?

Body game

Invite the children to cut up the pictures of people into the following body parts: heads, bodies, individual arms and individual legs, and then to sort them into sets. Children then take turns to roll the dice and collect the body part showing. As soon as a child has completed one body, he starts making another. See who can make the most bodies.

Things to ask

- How did you sort out your cut-up body parts?
- What happens if you roll another 'head' and you have one already?
- How many whole people did you make?
- How many arms and legs are there altogether in your 'bodies'?

Challenges

The game starts with the people assembled and the children take turns rolling the dice to take them apart.

The children collect body parts in order: head, body, legs and arms.

Can the child...

Sort the body parts?

Understand the instructions?

Count the body parts accurately?

Take turns rolling the dice?

You will need

- similar-sized pictures of people standing
- scissors
- a dice showing: a head, a body, a leg, a leg, an arm, an arm

how many?
altogether
one, two...
count
add
sort
group
set
part
whole

Maths learning

Say and use number names in order in familiar contexts

Count reliably up to ten everyday objects

Begin to use the vocabulary involved in adding and subtracting

Make a shape

During a PE session ask children in small groups to take turns exploring the different shapes they can make with their bodies. While you take photographs of the shapes, encourage the children to look at, talk about and draw each other's ideas. In the next PE session display the resulting pictures and photographs for the children to copy.

You will need

- PE mats
- a camera (optional)

long
tall
low
curved
straight
round
over
below
stretch
match
compare
position

Things to ask

- Bella says she has made a 'stand up' shape and Reuben has made a 'lie down' shape. Can you think of other ways to describe their shapes?
- Look at Simone's shape. Which parts of her body are touching the mat and which parts are not?
- How can you check that you are making the same shape as the one in the picture? Who could help you?
- Can you make a shape with two people? With three people?

Challenges

Suggest the children make number shapes with their bodies.

Challenge everybody in the group to join together to make a shape.

Can the child...

Talk about and describe her shape and those of others?

Think of a way to record her shape?

Observe and copy other children's ideas?

Work cooperatively with a partner?

Maths learning

Use developing mathematical ideas and methods to solve practical problems

Use language to describe the shape and size of solid shapes

Use everyday words to describe position

Where am I?

Ask each child to find a place to hide in the playground. Take photographs of all the children in their hiding places and later put the photographs in a book. Gather the children together. One by one, show the picture of each child's hiding place and invite that child to offer clues as to where it is. See if the other children can guess from the clues and photographs where his hiding place is.

You will need

- a camera
- resulting photographs
- a book for displaying photographs

how many?
position
under
below
on top
inside
behind
beside
next to
between

Things to ask

- Where do you think Sam is hiding? Why do you think that?
- What clues will help your friends to guess?
- How many people hid under/behind/next to/in front of something? How can we find out?
- How did you know where Amy was hiding?

Challenges

Ask each child to draw a map of where to find his hiding place.

Play a game of Sardines where one person hides and searchers join him in hiding.

Can the child...

Think of an appropriate place to hide?

Think of appropriate clues to give others?

Talk about the places where children have hidden?

Work cooperatively with other children?

Maths learning

Count reliably up to ten everyday objects

Use developing mathematical ideas and methods to solve practical problems

Use everyday words to describe position, direction and movement

Olympic counting

Invite groups of children to help you plan a 'use your body' session. Ask each group to think of and try out activities that involve counting and recording numbers — activities where each child can have a go. Make a few suggestions: counting numbers of steps along a bench or skips with a skipping rope. Ask the groups to discuss and record their results on a board.

You will need

- PE equipment: benches, balls, hoops, buckets, beanbags, skipping ropes
- a board or flipchart and pen
- paper and pencils

number
one, two...
how many?
count
altogether
lowest
highest
over
in
across

Things to ask

- How many steps did you take along the bench?
- What was the highest number you counted to?
- Which activity do you think people in your group liked best? How could we find out?
- How did you record the scores for skipping?

Challenges

Each group finds out the total number of beanbags they threw into a bucket.

Challenge the groups to rewrite their scores in order of lowest to highest.

Can the child...

Think of an activity that involves counting?

Count accurately?

Join in and talk about the counting involved in an activity?

Work cooperatively with other children?

Maths learning

Count reliably up to ten everyday objects

Use language to compare two numbers

Use developing mathematical ideas and methods to solve practical problems

Happy-face biscuits

Ask the children to spread a round cracker biscuit with cheese spread. They can add raisins for eyes, a piece of carrot for the nose, and half a cucumber slice for the mouth. Cress could be added as hair! Invite the children to eat their face-biscuits.

Things to ask

- How many raisins do you need?
- What shape are you making your mouth?
- How can we find out if there are enough biscuits for one each?
- How many biscuits are in the packet?

Challenges

Each child makes a second face that looks different from the first.

The children count how many eyes, noses and mouths there are altogether on two faces.

Can the child...

Use some shape words?

Use some number language spontaneously?

Count up to three or four items?

Work as part of a group?

You will need

- round cracker biscuits
- cheese spread
- raisins, carrots, cucumber and cress (optional)

one, two...
how many?
count
enough
shape
straight
round
circle
semi-circle
half

Maths learning

Count reliably up to ten everyday objects

Use developing mathematical ideas and methods to solve practical problems

Use language to describe the shape and size of flat shapes

Choose a colour

Place the six objects around the room where they can be seen. Put on some music and let the dancing begin! When the music stops, each child stands next to one of the objects. Next, roll the dice and record one point for each child standing by the object of that colour. Repeat several times, and discuss which object collected the most points.

Things to ask

- What does the dice show? So what shall we do next?
- Which colour is the most popular? Which is the least popular? How can you tell?
- Which colour are most children standing next to?
- Do you think there are more than or fewer than five children at green?

Challenges

Use objects in red, green, yellow and blue. When the music stops, one group of children records the results: one red cube for each child next to the red object and so on.

Ask the children to order the results from most to least popular colour.

Can the child...

Say some number names?

Estimate which colour has most children?

Use counting to solve the problem?

Join in the activity with understanding?

You will need

- a dice showing six different colours
- six large objects in the dice colours
- a board or flipchart and pens

count
estimate
how many?
one, two...
more
less
same
most
fewer
fewest
least
next to

Maths learning

Count reliably up to ten everyday objects

Use developing mathematical ideas and methods to solve practical problems

Use language to compare two quantities

The hoop shout

Place about six hoops on the ground and ask the children to stand in twos, threes, fours or fives inside them. Next the children skip around the hoops until you call out, "Hoop", and everyone stands in a hoop. A child from each group collects the numeral that matches his group number.

Things to ask

- How many children are in your hoop?
- Can you find the matching number in the bag?
- If two more people joined you in your hoop, how many would there be altogether?
- How could you work out how many children there are in two hoops?

Challenges

Roll a 1–6 dice. The winning hoop is the one with that number of children.

Call out a number. The children stand in groups of that number in the hoops.

Can the child...

Say how many children are in the hoop?

Find the matching numeral?

Work out how many there will be in the hoop when more children are added?

Work as part of a group?

You will need

- a bag of large numerals
- hoops

number
how many?
count
altogether
add
makes
matches
group
work out
one/two more

Maths learning

Recognise numerals 1 to 9

Begin to use the vocabulary involved in adding and subtracting

Begin to relate addition to combining two groups of objects

Bodies

You will need

- large cards showing a number of dots from 1 to 9
- large 3–10 number cards

number

how many?

count on

count back

pair

add

and

make

total

is the same as

different way

Maths learning

Begin to use the vocabulary involved in adding and subtracting

Begin to relate addition to combining two groups of objects

Use developing mathematical ideas and methods to solve practical problems

Get together

Give each child a dots card. Hold up a large number card and ask the children to get into pairs so that their dots total this number. Children without partners sit down. Involve everyone in checking the pairs of numbers, and see if any of those children sitting down can find a partner. Repeat with a different number card.

Things to ask

- What do Steph and Tessa's dots add up to?
- Lily is standing on the left and Ramesh is standing on the right. Will their dots still add up to the same if they swap places?
- Lola has got two dots. What number of dots should her partner have?
- How many different ways have we made seven?

Challenges

Give the children number cards instead of dots cards.

Ask the children to join up in threes to make the number on the card.

Can the child...

Find a partner to make the given number?

Self-check her ideas by counting?

Find a total by using counting on?

Talk about the activity when it is finished?

How long is the ribbon?

Each pair of children chooses a ribbon. Invite the children to find a part of their body that is the same length as the ribbon.

Things to ask

- What did you find that was the same length as your ribbon?
- What did you find that was shorter or longer than your ribbon?
- If you fold the ribbon in half, which parts of your body are the same length as this?
- How many times can you wind the ribbon round your wrist?

Challenges

Ask the children to record their measurements.

Challenge the children to measure something that is longer than the ribbon.

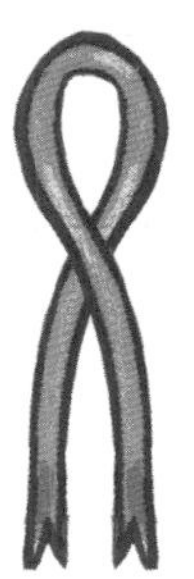

Can the child...

Understand the task?

Use the language of measures such as longer, shorter?

Find a way of successfully measuring different lengths?

Work cooperatively with a partner?

You will need

- a box of different-length ribbons

measure
compare
the same as
just over
just under
length
long
longer
shorter
half
compare
different

Maths learning

Use developing mathematical ideas and methods to solve practical problems

Use language to compare two quantities

Use language to compare the size and shape of solids and flat shapes

Planning and assessment

The mathematics covered in **Bodies**

Significant steps leading to the Early Learning Goals

	What are they doing?	How we've changed	Getting dressed	Body game	Make a shape	Where am I?	Olympic counting	Happy-face biscuits	Choose a colour	The hoop shout	Get together	How long is the ribbon?
Numbers (as labels and for counting)												
use some number names and number language	★	★	★	★	★	★	★	★	★	★	★	
count with some numbers in the correct order	★		★	★		★	★	★	★	★	★	
recognise groups with one, two or three objects	★			★				★	★	★	★	
count up to four objects by saying one number name for each	★			★		★	★	★	★	★	★	
represent numbers using fingers, pictures or marks on paper							★		★			
recognise numerals up to 9							★		★	★	★	
count out up to six objects from a larger group												
count up to or beyond ten objects				★		★	★	★	★	★	★	
Numbers (for calculating)												
compare two groups of objects and say when the groups are equal in number							★		★			
find the total number of items in two groups by counting all of them				★						★	★	
predict how many objects will be left when one or two are taken away												
say the number that is one more than a given number	★									★		
Shape and space												
use positional language to describe location and movement			★		★	★	★		★	★		★
select and use shapes appropriately for a given task								★				
choose to match similar shapes			★	★	★							
describe a simple journey						★	★					
select an example of a named shape			★	★	★							
show awareness of symmetry					★			★				
find 2D and 3D shapes that will fit together				★	★							
Measures												
use measuring language such as 'high', 'short', 'heavy' and words to describe time		★			★							★
talk about instruments we can use for measuring, such as hands and scales												★
order two or three items by length, height, weight or capacity												★

Flowers

This chapter has plenty of fantasy gardens to practise our counting in! We count the steps along a track to reach a rockery. We read numerals to find out how many flowers to plant, pick or water. While running a flower stall we write numerals, work out prices, and check the customers' orders. Meanwhile, customers do some sophisticated sums to work out which flowers they can buy. Finally, we have fun growing cress while discussing time.

Contents

Flowers

Let's sing

"In and out the dusty bluebells..."

Ask one of the children for a magic number. Then sing while with the 'leader' chooses her followers one at a time. When the magic number of children are moving around the circle, the song stops and the children go back to their places in the circle. Agree a new magic number and start the song again — the last child to join in last time can be the leader. Again, continue until the magic number is reached.

Can everyone remember the new magic number?

Let's do

Make some daisy chains

Each child makes a daisy chain. When everyone is finished, ask the children to join their daisy chains together to make a big circle for everyone to stand in.

How many daisies did you use?

Who has made the longest chain?

Can you wind your daisy chain around your head or around your wrist?

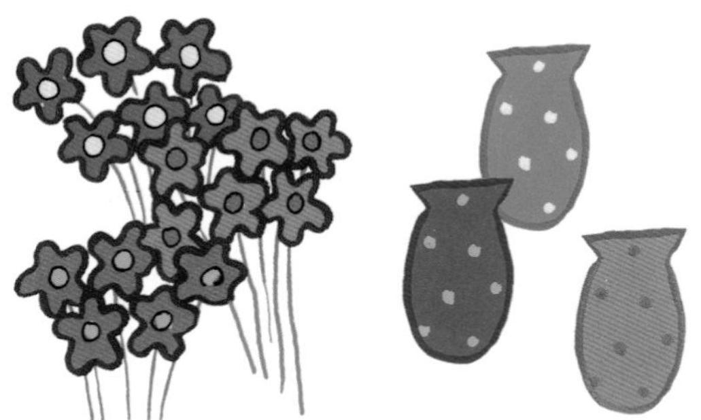

Flower arranging

Show the children a bunch of flowers and three vases and count the flowers together.

How many flowers should we put in each vase?

all together

Let's investigate

"What's in my garden?"

This is a memory game. The first child says, for example, "In my garden I have three watering cans." The next child repeats this and adds her own idea: "In my garden I have three watering cans, and two roses."

Planting bulbs

Help each child to plant a bulb in a flowerpot. Make a display of the planted flowerpots and use a calender to cross off the days before the first one starts to grow. Help the children to work out how long the shoot took to appear after planting. Next keep a record of how long it is before the last bulb starts to shoot. Make a big number line diary to record the answers to some of these questions.

On which day did the first shoot show?

What shapes are the leaves that emerge?

Are all the plants the same?

Which is the tallest/shortest plant? Can you measure them?

How much has your plant grown in a week/month?

Which bulb was the first to flower? How long was it after planting?

What is a good amount of water to give your bulb each day/week?

Window boxes

Give the children a 'window box' each to fill with flowers. Ask the children to make lots of different flowers using construction materials — such as plastic octagons and recycled materials. Afterwards encourage them to arrange the flowers in their window boxes using dough to hold them up.

You will need

- shoe boxes
- plastic straws
- buttons, plastic octagons, tissue paper, sticky paper shapes, jar lids, string…
- sticky tape/glue
- dough

shape
flat
circle
triangle
square
star
inside
outside
around
describe
explain

Things to ask

- What shapes did you use to make your flowers?
- How many flowers did you put in your box?
- Can you talk to your friend on the phone and describe the window box display you have made?
- Can you describe how to make one of your flowers?

Challenges

Ask the children to make a window box with ten flowers.

Can the children make flowers in matching pairs?

Can the child…

Count the number of flowers in her box?

Describe the shapes she used to make the flowers?

Use positional language with accuracy?

Select and use the materials successfully?

Maths learning

Count reliably up to ten everyday objects

Use language to describe the shape and size of flat shapes

Use everyday words to describe position

Flower number book

Show the children some flower and seed catalogues and invite them to join in counting all the yellow/red/purple flowers. The children then work in pairs to make their own 'flower counting book'. First ask each pair to make the book. Afterwards the children can stick down their own flowers: dried and pressed real flowers, pictures cut out from the catalogues, or their own drawings.

Things to ask

- Which numbers will you use in your book?
- How many flowers are you going to put on this page?
- Have you used the same number or different numbers on each page?
- Can you write the numeral that matches the number of flowers on this page?

Challenges

Suggest the children make a book for all the numbers up to ten.

Ask each pair to find out how many flowers there are altogether in the book.

Can the child...

Use number names and number language?

Represent numbers using pictures or marks?

Count beyond ten objects?

Work successfully with a partner?

You will need

- seed catalogues
- sugar paper
- scissors
- felt-tipped pens
- glue
- real flowers

number
how many?
one, two...
count
more
same
fewer
most
fewest
different

Maths learning

Count reliably up to ten everyday objects

Recognise numerals 1 to 9

Use language to compare two quantities

You will need

- real flowers
- three sticky paper circles per child
- sticky paper petals in a box
- a 1–3 dice

number
how many?
one, two...
count
more
same
fewer
most
fewest
altogether

Maths learning

Say and use number names in order in familiar contexts

Count reliably up to ten everyday objects

Use developing mathematical ideas and methods to solve practical problems

Petals

Before playing the 'flower game', ask the children to help you count the petals of real flowers. Afterwards give each child three paper circles and place the petals in a box nearby. The children then take turns to roll the dice and collect that number of petals to stick on the outside of their circles. When a child's flower has six petals, she starts another. The first to complete three flowers is the winner.

Things to ask

- What number does the dice say?
- Which flower has the most/fewest petals?
- How many petals are on your flower?
- How many more petals do you need to finish the flower?

Challenges

Challenge the children to make flowers with ten petals.

The children progress to using a 1–6 dice.

Can the child...

Use number names and number language?

Count up to six objects?

Count with some numbers in the right order?

Understand the need to take turns during the game?

Cress people

Ask the children to collect empty egg shells and egg cartons. Each child fills two egg shells with damp cotton wool and sprinkles on some cress seeds. Next he draws the faces with felt-tipped pens and places his eggs inside two sections of an egg carton. Finally he makes a cone-shaped hat from a small circle of paper, slit cut to the centre and fastened with sticky tape or a staple. Cress 'hair' will grow underneath.

Things to ask

- How many hats will you need to make?
- What shape did you use to make a hat?
- How many hats do you and your friend need to make altogether?
- Do you think it took a long or short time for the cress to grow?

Challenges

Challenge the children to write a number on the cone hat.

Give the children a three-section egg carton and ask them to work out how many different ways the two egg shells will fit.

Can the child...

Name the 2D and 3D shapes (circle and cone)?

Work out how many hats are needed altogether?

Use number language in conversation?

Carry out the activity with reasonable care?

You will need

- two empty egg shells per child
- cotton wool
- cress seed
- felt-tipped pens
- egg cartons
- paper circles
- sticky tape or stapler

how many?
one, two...
time
day
quickly
slowly
long time
short time
shape
cone
circle

Maths learning

Count reliably up to ten everyday objects

Use developing mathematical ideas and methods to solve practical problems

Use language to describe the shape and size of solids and flat shapes

You will need

- a water tray
- 1–6 plastic numerals
- plastic flowers in a box
- flowerpots with no drainage holes
- watering cans

one, two...
number
count
most
fewest
add
make
how many more?
check

Maths learning

Count reliably up to ten everyday objects

Recognise numerals 1 to 9

Begin to use the vocabulary involved in adding and subtracting

Watering the flowers

Half-fill the water tray and add the plastic numerals. Invite the children to collect a number from the water tray and to count out that number of flowers from the bowl. The children can then put the flowers in a flowerpot and water them with the watering can.

Things to ask

- What does that number say?
- How can you check that the right number of flowers are in the pot?
- How many more flowers do you need to add to make your number?
- Which pot contains the most flowers?

Challenges

Each child adds another flower to her pot, works out how many flowers she has and finds the correct numeral.

Ask the children to put the pots in order from 'fewest flowers' to 'most flowers'.

Can the child...

Recognise some of the numerals?

Count the correct number of flowers consistently?

Check her own work?

Use the water tray and materials appropriately?

Sunflower number line

Ask the children to paint — and later cut out — some large sunflower heads. Write a numeral (from 1 to 10) on each flower centre and attach a stem made from the green paper. Ask each child to find their flower, look at their number, and make that many leaves. Afterwards invite the children to put all the flowers in order to make a sunflower number line.

Things to ask

- Which number is on your sunflower?
- How many leaves do you need on your stem?
- Which sunflower has the most leaves?
- How many sunflowers are there altogether?

Challenges

Challenge the children to invent a sunflower number line game.

Ask the children to put the right number of plastic minibeasts on each sunflower to match the number on the flower.

Can the child...

Recognise numerals 1–10?

Make the correct number of leaves?

Use the language of number order such as 'before', 'after', 'next'?

Take part in the organisation of the number line?

You will need

- paper for painting
- paints
- a marker pen
- green paper
- scissors
- glue

number
count
before
after
next
most
fewest
add
altogether
how many more?

Maths learning

Count reliably up to ten everyday objects

Recognise numerals 1 to 9

Use language to compare two numbers

Flowers

Wild flowers

You will need

- a garden (sheet of green card)
- forty counters
- fifteen 1–3 number cards
- five cards showing a wolf

The children pretend the counters are flowers and 'plant' them all over the garden. Next shuffle all twenty cards and place them face down on the table. Players take one card at a time, read the number out loud, and pick that many flowers. If they turn over a wolf card they have to put three flowers back. The game is over when one player has picked ten flowers. That player wins.

number
how many?
how many more?
more
add
make
collect
altogether
take away
how many are left?

Things to ask

- How many flowers have you collected?
- How many more flowers do you need to make ten?
- How many flowers would you have left if you picked up a wolf card?
- How many flowers are left in the garden? Guess first, then count.

Challenges

The children use a set of cards showing numerals 1–5.

Change the value of the wolf cards and also the total number of cards needed for the children to win.

Can the child...

Count accurately throughout the game?

Read numerals 1–3?

Estimate the number of flowers in the garden at a given time?

Explain what is happening to the number of flowers she has during the game?

Maths learning

Count reliably up to ten everyday objects

Begin to use the vocabulary involved in adding and subtracting

Begin to relate addition to combining two groups of objects

Build a rockery

Give each pair of children the stepping stones to make a track. The children take it in turns to roll the 1–3 dice, pick up a pebble and move it that number of steps along the track. Children must roll the exact number at the end of the track to move into the 'rockery' and then start again with another pebble. Play continues until all ten pebbles are in the rockery.

Things to ask

- How many steps must you take?
- How can you find out how many pebbles there are in your rockery?
- If you have seven pebbles in the rockery, how many more pebbles are there to move?
- If you roll a two, will you reach the rockery?

Challenges

Add more stepping stones and give the children a 1–6 dice.

Give the children two 1–3 dice and challenge them to work out the combined numbers.

Can the child...

Explain how to play the game?

Count the appropriate number of steps?

Say how many more to make ten?

Work cooperatively with a partner?

You will need

- ten large paper 'stepping stones' per pair
- ten pebbles per pair
- a 1–3 dice per pair

one, two...

how many?

(not) enough

nearly

count

start at

finish

how many are left?

how many more to make?

Maths learning

Count reliably up to ten everyday objects

Begin to use the vocabulary involved in adding and subtracting

Use developing mathematical ideas and methods to solve practical problems

Place your order

The children pretend to be florists. Give each child a written order for a bunch of flowers indicating the colours you want and the number of each colour. When the child has prepared the arrangement help her to check it against your order.

Things to ask

- What does that order say?
- How many red flowers did I order? Is that what you've given me?
- How did you know how many yellow flowers were needed?
- How many flowers did I order altogether?

Challenges

The children write out their own orders for each other to make up and check.

Ask the children to make an arrangement of flowers and record on paper which flowers they have used.

Can the child...

Follow the instructions consistently?

Find a way to check her work?

Write out appropriate orders that the other children can understand?

Actively take part in the role play?

Flowers

You will need

- flowers made from straws and tissue paper — in a variety of single colours
- vases
- paper and pencils

how many?
(not) enough
too many
count
add
one/two more
altogether
take away
one/two less
check

Maths learning

Count reliably up to ten everyday objects

Recognise numerals 1 to 9

Begin to use the vocabulary involved in adding and subtracting

The flower stall

Put up a notice on the stall: 'red flowers...1p; yellow flowers...2p' and ask one of the older children, or a helper, to be the florist. Give each remaining child five pennies to spend on flowers at the stall. Afterwards, discuss and record the different combinations of flowers each child bought with his five pennies.

Things to ask

- What did you buy with your five pennies?
- How many flowers did you buy, George? Did everybody buy the same number of flowers as George?
- How did Cayo manage to buy more flowers than George?
- Can you make a record of the flowers you have bought?

Challenges

Add additional prices for the children to work with: 'orange flowers...3p; purple flowers...4p'.

Challenge the children to work out how many flowers they could buy with 10p.

Can the child...

Spend all of his coins each time?

Explain what he is going to buy and how much each flower costs?

Make a record of what he has spent?

Join in the activity with understanding?

You will need

- two vases
- red flowers and yellow flowers made from tissue paper
- paper and marker pens
- five 1p coins per child

how many?
more
same
penny
price
cost
buy
spend
pay
how much?
costs the same as

Maths learning

Count reliably up to ten everyday objects

Recognise numerals 1 to 9

Use language to compare two quantities

Seed packets

Show the children a selection of seed packets and count and discuss the contents. Invite each child to make her own packet of seeds from a folded sheet of paper and sticky tape. Ask a child to help you count some chick peas into her packet. Then she can write the number on the packet as a label.

You will need

- A4 paper and felt-tipped pens
- sticky tape
- chick peas

number
one, two...
how many?
count
one more than
one less than
comes before
comes after
read
write

Things to ask

- How many chick peas have you got in your packet?
- How will we know how many seeds are in your packet?
- Can you write the number 5?
- Which number comes after 5?

Challenges

Challenge the children to make a 1–10 number line using seed packets showing this range of numbers.

Mix up the seed packets and ask the children to reorder them from 1–10.

Can the child...

Recognise numerals up to 9?

Represent numbers making marks on paper?

Say the number that is one more than the given number?

Organise the materials: paper, scissors, sticky tape?

Maths learning

Count reliably up to ten everyday objects

Recognise numerals 1 to 9

Find one more or one less than a number from 1 to 10

The flower beds game

Put the flower beds on the table. Players take turns to roll both dice, read the number and shape and put that number of flowers in the flower bed of the correct shape. The game ends when all the flowers have gone. Next, players guess which flower bed contains the most flowers, and then count them to check.

Things to ask

- What do the two dice say? So what must you do?
- Which flower bed do you think has the most flowers? Which has the fewest?
- How could we find out how many flowers there are in the circle-shaped bed?
- Can you explain how to play the game?

Challenges

The group uses a 1–6 dice and more flowers.

Players empty the flower beds by taking the number of flowers that the dice tells them from the bed.

Can the child...

Count out the flowers accurately?

Talk about the shapes of the flower beds?

Talk about which flower bed has the most flowers, and which has the fewest?

Explain how to play the game?

You will need

- three 'flower beds' (different shaped pieces of card)
- a pot of twenty paper flowers
- a 1–3 dice
- a dice showing the flower bed shapes

number
same
compare
most
fewest
shape
circle
triangle
square
rectangle
explain

Maths learning

Count reliably up to ten everyday objects

Use language to compare two quantities

Use language to describe the shape and size of flat shapes

Planning and assessment

The mathematics covered in **Flowers**

Significant steps leading to the Early Learning Goals

	Window boxes	Flower number book	Petals	Cress people	Watering the flowers	Sunflower number line	Wild flowers	Build a rockery	Place your order	The flower stall	Seed packets	The flower beds game
Numbers (as labels and for counting)												
use some number names and number language	★	★	★	★	★	★	★	★	★	★	★	★
count with some numbers in the correct order	★	★	★	★	★	★	★	★	★	★	★	★
recognise groups with one, two or three objects	★	★		★		★	★		★	★		★
count up to four objects by saying one number name for each	★	★	★	★	★	★	★	★	★	★	★	★
represent numbers using fingers, pictures or marks on paper		★								★	★	
recognise numerals up to 9		★			★	★	★		★	★	★	
count out up to six objects from a larger group		★	★		★	★	★		★	★		★
count up to or beyond ten objects		★				★	★	★	★		★	★
Numbers (for calculating)												
compare two groups of objects and say when the groups are equal in number		★			★					★		★
find the total number of items in two groups by counting all of them				★					★		★	
predict how many objects will be left when one or two are taken away												
say the number that is one more than a given number											★	
Shape and space												
use positional language to describe location and movement	★			★				★				
select and use shapes appropriately for a given task	★										★	★
choose to match similar shapes												★
describe a simple journey												
select an example of a named shape												★
show awareness of symmetry	★		★			★						
find 2D and 3D shapes that will fit together	★			★								
Measures												
use measuring language such as ‘high’, ‘short’, ‘heavy’ and words to describe time				★								
talk about instruments we can use for measuring, such as hands and scales												
order two or three items by length, height, weight or capacity												

Pennies

In this chapter we discuss the size, shape and weight of certain coins. We learn their names and their values in relation to one another. We use purses to sort our money into certain amounts, and sometimes ask other people to guess how much money is inside! There are plenty of opportunities for games, counting, recording and spending our money — but not before we've been encouraged to think about saving it!

Contents

Pennies

Let's sing

"Five currant buns in the baker's shop..."

Sing the song and do the actions using large card — or dough — currant buns and real pennies. Stop every now and then to count the buns, customers and pennies. Each time — ask different children to get ready the correct number of buns, pennies and customers.

What if you have seven currant buns? How many pennies would we need to sing the song then?

Let's do

Old gold

Ask the children to bring in any coins or paper money they have from other countries to show and talk about. Compare an old penny with a present-day penny. What do the children notice?

Can anyone bring in some coins from long ago?

What happens if we put tracing paper over the coins and rub with wax crayons?

"How many pennies?"

Hide a number of pennies in your pocket. Once on the carpet, ask the children if they can find out how many pennies are in your pocket by asking you questions.

Which questions are useful to ask?

all together

Let's investigate

"Why do we have money?"

Discuss things that we need money for and things we don't.

Do we need money to buy sweets from the shop? To go for a swing in the park? To take a trip on a bus? To collect autumn leaves?

Penny prints

Press both sides of a penny down onto a flat piece of modelling clay or dough. Also try using other coins.

Do both sides of the penny print the same?

Shiny pennies

Put pennies in fizzy cola drink and leave them until the next day to make them shine.

A hundred pennies

Put 100 pennies in a shallow tray for the children to play with. Encourage the children to count them, group them, pile them... At the end of the day share ideas for things to do with the coins.

How can we check there are still a hundred pennies? Let's try out Sharma's idea.

Pennies

You will need

- shoe boxes with a slit cut in each lid
- lots of 1p, 2p, 5p, 10p coins

larger
smaller
sort
match
coin
penny
shape
round
circle
the same as
different

Maths learning

Use developing mathematical ideas and methods to solve practical problems

Use language to compare two quantities

Use language to describe the shape and size of flat shapes

Coin boxes

Show the children some boxes with a different coin stuck on each lid. Give each pair of children some coins to 'post' into the boxes displaying the matching coins. When the children have matched and posted all the coins, ask them to check the contents of one box at a time to make sure all the coins are the same.

Things to ask

- Are these coins the same?
- Can you tell me the names of these coins?
- Into which box would you post a penny ?
- How can you check that all the coins in this box are the same?

Challenges

Give the children more, or different, coins.

Ask the children to write a label for each box to show which coins should be posted into the box.

Can the child...

Tell you the names of some coins?

Sort and match the coins consistently?

Talk about her observations of the coins?

Stay with the task until it is finished?

In the bag

Gather the children together and pass one of each type of coin around for them to touch. Next hold up a small cloth bag and ask the children to help you put a mixture of coins — including some 1p coins — inside. Ask a child to put his hand into the bag to feel for — and take out — as many 1p coins as he can find.

Things to ask

- Is a 1p coin heavier/lighter/larger/smaller than a 10p coin?
- How many pennies have you found so far?
- How many pennies do you think are left in the bag?
- How will you know when you have found all the pennies in the bag? How can you check?

Challenges

Ask the children to fill bags with coins for others to find pennies.

Challenge the children to name all the coins that are in the bag.

Can the child...

Explain how he is trying to find the pennies?

Count the pennies he has found so far?

Talk about the differences between coins of different value?

Carry out the activity confidently?

You will need

- 1p, 10p and 50p coins
- hand-sized cloth bags

how many?
coin
penny
size
the same
different
heavier
lighter
weight
shape
round

Maths learning

Count reliably up to ten everyday objects

Use developing mathematical ideas and methods to solve practical problems

Use language to describe the shape and size of flat shapes

Pennies

You will need

- one coin grid per child
- 1p coins
- a 1–3 dice

number

one, two...

how many?

count

coin

penny

arrange

collect

enough

altogether

how many more?

Maths learning

Count reliably up to ten everyday objects

Begin to use the vocabulary involved in adding and subtracting

Use developing mathematical ideas and methods to solve practical problems

Penny game

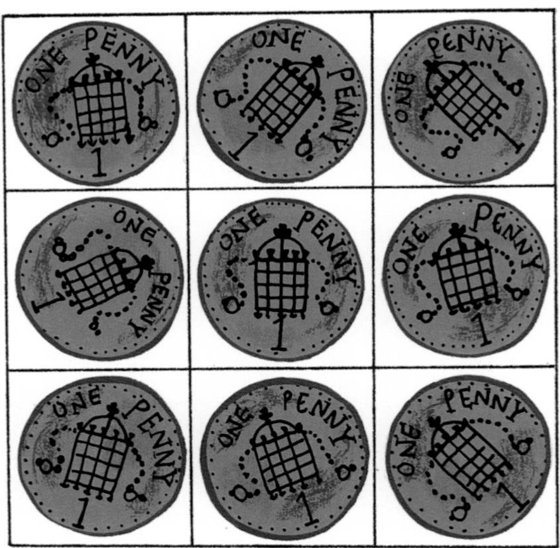

Give each child a coin grid and nine 1p coins. The children then take turns to roll the 1–3 dice, collecting that number of 1p coins to put on their grids. Continue until everyone has filled the spaces on their grids — but make sure the final dice roll matches the number of empty spaces.

Things to ask

- What number does the dice say?
- How many pennies did you pick up?
- How many more pennies do you need to fill the grid?
- You've rolled a 2 on the dice. Is that enough to finish?

Challenges

Challenge the children to play the game in reverse by taking coins off the grid?

Give the children 2p coins to use.

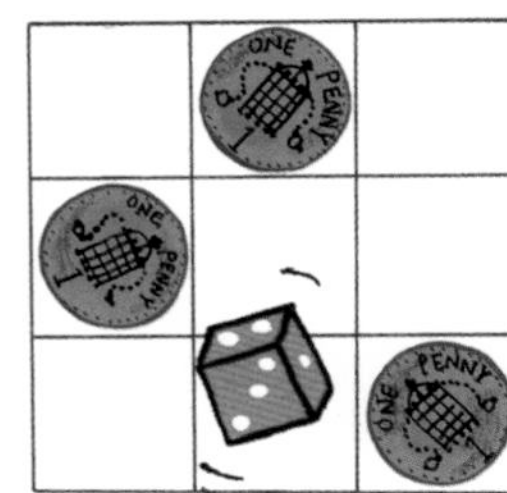

Can the child...

Recognise the dot patterns on the dice.

Count an irregular arrangement of 1p coins?

Show an interest in number problems?

Concentrate on the activity?

How much?

This activity can be done individually or in pairs. Hide a number of 1p coins in each purse. The children have to open each purse, count the coins inside and decide how to show this number on a label that they then stick onto the purse. Encourage the children to invent and use their own ideas for recording. Later, all the children can show their purses and ask if anyone can tell how many pennies are inside.

Things to ask

- How many pennies are in this purse? How could you show that number on the label?
- How can you check your work each time?
- How many pennies should you put in this purse? How do you know?
- Why is it important to make your label as clear and neat as you can?

Challenges

The children can make up labels for empty purses. Their partners have to read these labels and then put the correct number of pennies inside each purse.

Challenge the children to make a money number line by pegging nine purses containing 1–9 pennies in order on a washing line.

Can the child...

Count accurately?

Think of and use a clear method to record the number?

Check his answers?

Work cooperatively with a partner?

You will need

- fabric purses
- a quantity of 1p coins
- sticky labels
- pencils

how many?
count
coin
penny
pence
show
read
write
check
work out
record

Maths learning

Count reliably up to ten everyday objects

Recognise numerals 1 to 9

Use developing mathematical ideas and methods to solve practical problems

Pennies

You will need

- a 2 × 5 grid 'playing board'
- ten 1p coins per player
- a dice marked '1p, 1p, 2p, 5p, 10p, 10p'
- a pot

how many?
one, two...
count
work out
more
fewer
take away
how many are left?
the same as
coins
penny

Maths learning

Count reliably up to ten everyday objects

Begin to use the vocabulary involved in adding and subtracting

Begin to relate subtraction to 'taking away'

Pennies in the pot

This is a game for two to four players. Each player takes a playing board and places a penny in each space. Players then take turns to roll the dice. If the dice shows '1p', the player takes one of her pennies off the board and puts it into the pot; if the dice shows any other amount, the pennies stay on the grid. The winner is the first player to put all of her coins in the pot.

Things to ask

- What does the dice show?
- How many pennies do you have left?
- How many pennies have you given away so far? How can you tell?
- Has Millie given away more or fewer pennies than Alfie? How do you know?

Challenges

Encourage the children to play the game in reverse by putting coins onto the grids.

The children play the game using a combination of coins with the money dice. Players remove coins that match — or that can be added together to make — the amount on the dice.

Can the child...

Make up the correct amounts in 1p coins?

Count how many pennies she has left?

Work out how many of her pennies have gone?

Work well in a group?

The currant bun game

This is a game for two to four players. Put the buns in a basket labelled '1p each'. Players take turns to roll the dice, read out the dice-number, and collect that many pennies from the pot. After each round everyone exchanges his pennies for the same number of buns. Play continues until all the buns have gone. At the end of the game players count up how many buns they have bought.

Things to ask

- What number does the dice show? How many pennies do you need to take?
- Can you show us how you count your pennies?
- How many pennies do you have? So how many buns can you buy?
- Jacob bought seven buns. How much did he spend? How do you know?

Challenges

Explain to the children that you are putting up the price of the buns to 2p each.

Make a list of bakery shop cakes and invite the children to buy them when the pot of 1p coins is empty.

Can the child...

Count his 1p coins accurately?

Exchange his coins for the correct number of buns?

Explain a method for counting pennies?

Take part in the activity with understanding?

You will need

- 'currant buns' made from dough
- a pot of 1p coins
- a basket
- a 1–3 dice

number
how many?
count (up)
coin
penny
price
cost
buy
spend
how much?
show me

Maths learning

Say and use number names in order in familiar contexts

Count reliably up to ten everyday objects

Use developing mathematical ideas and methods to solve practical problems

The mystery purse

Put some pennies in a purse or zip-up bag. Pass it round the group and ask the children to feel it and guess how much money is inside. Open up the purse and count the pennies together. Give children purses to fill. Ask them to count the pennies and write the number on a label.

You will need

- fabric purses — one per person
- a large quantity of 1p coins
- sticky labels
- pencils

one, two...
how many?
count
more
fewer
money
coin
penny
show me
guess
heavier
lighter

Things to ask

- How many pennies do you think are in the purse?
- Can you show me the numbers with your fingers as we count the coins together?
- How do you work out how many pennies you need to fill your purse?
- Do you think there are more/fewer coins in this purse than in that purse?

Challenges

The children use 1p coins and 2p coins to fill their purses.

Give the children purses — labelled with amounts for them to count out and put inside.

Can the child...

Make a sensible estimate of number?

Write a numeral to match the number of pennies?

Explain how she knew how much was in the purse?

Join in with the counting activity?

Maths learning

Count reliably up to ten everyday objects

Use developing mathematical ideas and methods to solve practical problems

Use language to compare two quantities

Make a snake

Show the children how to lay out some pennies to make a snake. Then encourage them to make their own snakes, counting the pennies in each one by one. Afterwards give each child some dough to make the eyes and tongue. Display the children's work on a flat surface using Blu-Tack to keep the pennies in place.

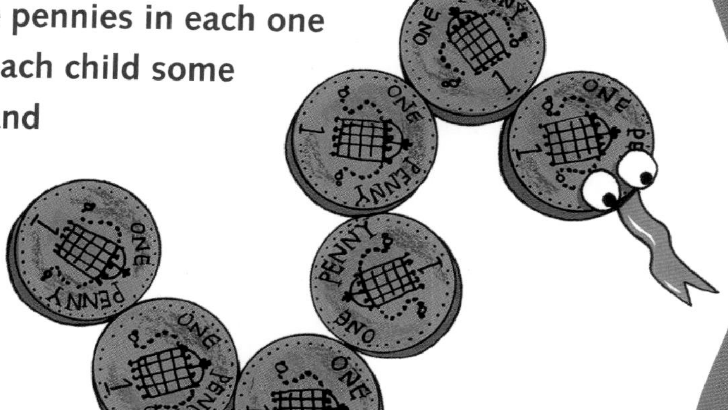

Things to ask

- Which is the longest/shortest snake?
- How many pennies have you used to make this snake? Can you make another snake using more/fewer pennies?
- How many of these snakes are made with seven pennies?
- How much is that snake worth?

Challenges

The children could try recording their snakes by drawing around the pennies and colouring in the circles.

Use 2p coins, or a mixture of 1p and 2p coins. Children try to work out how much their snakes are worth.

Can the child...

Compare different snakes and talk about their lengths?

Count the number of pennies used to make each snake?

Explain the connection between the length of the snake and the number of pennies?

Explore other ideas for making snakes?

Pennies

You will need

- a large quantity of 1p coins
- dough
- Blu-Tack

more
fewer
most
fewest
penny
longer
shorter
longest
shortest
how many?
how much?
worth

Maths learning

Count reliably up to ten everyday objects

Use developing mathematical ideas and methods to solve practical problems

Use language to compare two quantities

Pennies

You will need

- small paper plates
- twenty 1p coins
- a 1–3 dice

count
how many?
altogether
more
fewer
most
fewest
leaves
left
take away
penny
next to

Maths learning

Begin to relate subtraction to 'taking away'

Use language to compare two quantities

Use everyday words to describe position, direction and movement

Pass the pennies

This is a game for three or four players. Players begin by counting five pennies onto their paper plates. Players then take turns to roll the dice and give that number of pennies to the player on their left. The dice circulates round the group five times. Players then count up the pennies on their plates.

Things to ask

- How many pennies do you need to give to the player sitting next to you?
- How many pennies have you got altogether?
- Have you got more or fewer pennies than you started with? How do you know?
- Do you think the winner should be the player with the most or the fewest pennies? Why?

Challenges

Give the children ten pennies to start with and a 1–6 dice.

Suggest the children play the game for five minutes and then count the pennies.

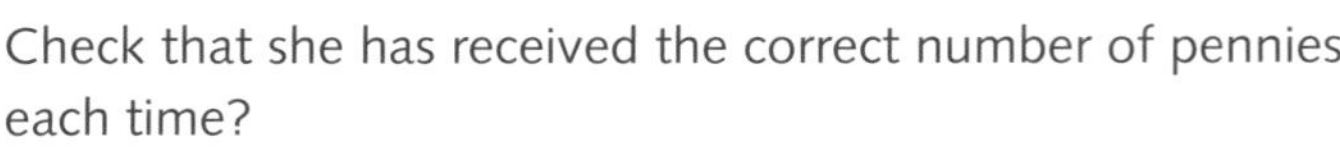

Can the child...

Pass on the correct number of pennies each time?

Check that she has received the correct number of pennies each time?

Say whether she has more or fewer pennies than at the start?

Explain how to play the game?

Pennies trail

Two players put a counter each on 'Start' and two pennies in all the trail spaces. They take turns to roll the dice and move their counters that number of steps. When a player lands on a space he collects a penny and puts it in his purse. If the dice shows a penny, he counts the pennies in his purse but doesn't move his counter. When a player reaches the 'Finish' square, count who has the most pennies.

Things to ask

- How many pennies have you each got? Who has the most/fewest?
- How many pennies are still on the trail? Can you count them in twos?
- Does the first player to reach the finish always have the most pennies? Why is that?
- Can you think of another way to work out who has the most/fewest pennies?

Challenges

Challenge the children to draw their own trails.

The children play the game using 2p coins.

Can the child...

Move along the trail counting one space at a time?

Count in twos?

Explain when you can/cannot collect a penny?

Tell someone else how to play the game?

You will need

- a long piece of card marked with twenty spaces
- forty 1p coins
- two counters
- two purses
- a dice marked '1, 2, 3, 4, 5, penny'

start

finish

more

fewer

most

fewest

penny

count in ones/twos

how many?

Maths learning

Count reliably up to ten everyday objects

Use developing mathematical ideas and methods to solve practical problems

Use language to compare two quantities

Pennies

You will need

- a 3 × 3 playing grid per player
- pot of 1p coins
- pot of 2p coins
- a 1–3 dice

how many?

count in ones/twos

add

make

money

coin

penny

pence

exchange

the same as

Maths learning

Count reliably up to ten everyday objects

Use language to compare two numbers

Begin to use the vocabulary involved in adding and subtracting

Saving boards

Players take turns to roll the dice, say the number, and collect that number of 1p coins from the pot. When a player has two pennies she must say, "Exchange!" and exchange the two 1p coins for a 2p coin which she then places on her playing board. The game ends when one player has filled up her grid.

Things to ask

- What is saving? What might you need to save up for?
- How many pennies have you got? Can you do an exchange yet?
- How many 2p coins are there on your board?
- How can you count the money?

Challenges

Suggest the children play the game using 1p and 5p coins and a 1–6 dice.

Ask the children to play using 1p and 10p coins and a 1–6 dice.

Can the child...

Understand when and how to exchange her coins?

Remember that '2' on the dice means collect two 1p coins — not a 2p coin?

Work out a way to count the money on the board?

Explain how to play the game?

Spend or save?

The children take turns to roll the dice, say the number, and collect that number of pennies. Each time the teacher asks the player if he wants to 'spend or save?', giving him an opportunity to buy something from the shop or to wait and save up for something else. After a while the teacher asks the children to stop to look at — and discuss — how they have used their money.

Things to ask

- How many pennies have you got now?
- Have you got enough to buy a cube yet?
- Becky has 7p. How much more does she need to buy a pencil?
- Which things did you have to save for? Why?

Challenges

Ask the children to collect and price more expensive items.

Invite the children to write a shopping list before the game, or a sales invoice after the game.

Can the child...

Read the prices on the labels?

Count accurately?

Talk about what he has spent or saved?

Make decisions about what he is going to do?

Pennies

You will need

- a 1–6 dice
- a pot of 1p coins
- a collection of objects 'for sale' at prices up to 10p

how much?
enough
penny
pence
price
cost
buy
spend
pay
save

Maths learning

Recognise numerals 1 to 9

Use language to compare two numbers

Use developing mathematical ideas and methods to solve practical problems

Planning and assessment

The mathematics covered in **Pennies**

Significant steps leading to the Early Learning Goals

	Coin boxes	In the bag	Penny game	How much?	Pennies in the pot	The currant bun game	The mystery purse	Make a snake	Pass the pennies	Pennies trail	Saving boards	Spend or save?
Numbers (as labels and for counting)												
use some number names and number language	★	★	★	★	★	★	★	★	★	★	★	★
count with some numbers in the correct order		★	★	★	★	★	★	★	★	★	★	★
recognise groups with one, two or three objects				★	★	★	★	★	★		★	★
count up to four objects by saying one number name for each		★	★	★	★	★	★	★	★	★	★	★
represent numbers using fingers, pictures or marks on paper				★			★					
recognise numerals up to 9				★	★		★					★
count out up to six objects from a larger group		★						★	★		★	★
count up to or beyond ten objects			★	★	★		★	★	★	★	★	★
Numbers (for calculating)												
compare two groups of objects and say when the groups are equal in number					★			★	★	★		
find the total number of items in two groups by counting all of them												
predict how many objects will be left when one or two are taken away												
say the number that is one more than a given number												
Shape and space												
use positional language to describe location and movement	★	★							★			
select and use shapes appropriately for a given task								★				
choose to match similar shapes	★	★										
describe a simple journey												
select an example of a named shape		★										
show awareness of symmetry												
find 2D and 3D shapes that will fit together								★				
Measures												
use measuring language such as 'high', 'short', 'heavy' and words to describe time	★	★					★	★				
talk about instruments we can use for measuring, such as hands and scales												
order two or three items by length, height, weight or capacity		★					★	★		★		

Further reading

MiniMaths 1
Kim Connor
BEAM Education 2000

Learning Mathematics in the Nursery: Desirable Approaches
the Early Childhood Mathematics Group
BEAM Education 1997

Extending Thought in Young Children: A Parent-Teacher Partnership
C Athey
Paul Chapman 1990

Mathematics for Young Children: An Active Thinking Approach
M H Bird
Routledge 1991

Mathematical Beginnings: Problem Solving for Young Children
J Blinko and N Graham
Claire Publications 1988

Exploring Mathematics with Younger Children
(an ATM Activity Book)
Association of Teachers of Mathematics 1991

Number in the Nursery and Reception
S Gifford with P Barber and S Ebbutt
BEAM Education 1998

Teaching Numeracy: Maths in the Primary Classroom
edited by R Merttens
Scholastic 1996

Teaching Mathematics to Young Children: 4–7
C Mitchell and H Williams
Chris Kington Publishing 1998

Nursery Mathematics: A Development for 3–5 Year Olds
Heinemann Maths Plus 1997

Supporting Mathematical Development in the Early Years
L Pound
Oxford University Press 1999

Teaching and Learning Early Number
edited by I Thompson
Oxford University Press 1997

Teaching the Early Years
H Williams, C Skinner and P Barber
Rigby 2000

Curriculum Guidance for the Foundation Stage
Qualifications and Curriculum Authority
Department for Education and Employment 2000
QCA/00/587

early learning goals

	Wheels												Shoes												Sand				
	Roll out	Fishing for wheels	Spokes to the centre	Do the rounds	Making tracks	Number wheels	Print rollers	Traffic jam	Car park	Intercity trains	Roadway	Bus stop	Pairs	Whose shoes?	Sock washing line	Match the prints	Find the footprints	Shoe filling	Living in a shoe	Shoe boxes	Grandma's footsteps	Lace them up	Shoe shop	Do up your shoes	Sandy numbers	Hidden numbers	Fences	Give away potfuls	Sieve it out
Say and use number names in order in familiar contexts	★	★	★	★			★	★	★	★	★	★	★		★		★	★	★	★	★	★	★	★	★	★	★	★	★
Count reliably up to ten everyday objects	★	★	★	★			★	★	★	★		★	★		★		★	★	★	★	★	★		★		★	★	★	★
Recognise numerals 1 to 9			★			★					★	★								★			★		★	★			
Use language to compare two numbers						★												★		★	★		★						★
Begin to use the vocabulary involved in adding and subtracting								★		★		★										★		★			★	★	
Find one more or one less than a number from 1 to 10								★															★		★				
Begin to relate addition to combining two groups of objects								★	★	★		★										★		★			★		
Begin to relate subtraction to 'taking away'								★				★												★					
Talk about, recognise and recreate simple patterns	★				★		★				★					★													
Use developing mathematical ideas and methods to solve practical problems		★	★	★	★			★	★	★	★	★	★	★	★	★		★	★	★	★	★	★	★			★	★	★
Use language to compare two quantities	★	★						★	★	★				★	★	★	★	★	★	★	★			★				★	★
Use language to describe the shape and size of solids and flat shapes	★	★		★	★		★						★	★									★		★	★	★		★
Use everyday words to describe position, direction and movement		★	★	★	★	★	★				★					★	★	★	★		★	★		★	★				

Planning and assessment

This chart cross-references the activities in MiniMaths to the Early Learning Goals. These are identified by the QCA (Qualifications and Curriculum Authority) as the levels of attainment that children should have reached by the end of their Reception year. For more detailed assessment of the significant steps leading to the Early Learning Goals, please refer to the chart at the end of each chapter.

							Bodies											Flowers													Pennies										
Sandcastle straws	Sand writing	Hide the treasure	Lucky dip	Flags	Finding how many	What's it worth?	What are they doing?	How we've changed	Getting dressed	Body game	Make a shape	Where am I?	Olympic counting	Happy-face biscuits	Choose a colour	The hoop shout	Get together	How long is the ribbon?	Window boxes	Flower number book	Petals	Cress people	Watering the flowers	Sunflower number line	Wild flowers	Build a rockery	Place your order	The flower stall	Seed packets	The flower beds game	Coin boxes	In the bag	Penny game	How much?	Pennies in the pot	The currant bun game	The mystery purse	Make a snake	Pass the pennies	Pennies trail	Saving boards	Spend or save?
★	★		★	★	★	★	★	★	★	★		★	★	★	★	★	★		★	★	★	★	★	★	★	★	★	★	★	★		★	★	★	★	★	★	★	★	★	★	★
★			★	★	★	★	★			★		★	★	★	★	★	★		★	★	★	★	★	★	★	★	★	★	★	★		★	★	★	★	★	★	★	★	★	★	★
	★		★		★								★		★	★	★			★			★	★	★		★	★	★					★			★					★
													★		★					★				★																	★	★
★					★	★				★						★	★				★		★	★	★	★	★	★					★		★				★		★	★
	★						★									★													★													
			★		★											★	★								★		★															
★																									★										★				★			
				★			★		★					★																	★											
		★	★	★	★	★		★	★	★	★	★	★	★	★	★	★	★			★	★	★	★	★	★	★		★		★	★	★	★	★	★	★	★	★	★	★	★
★		★				★		★							★			★		★	★		★	★				★		★	★				★		★	★	★	★	★	
	★	★									★			★				★	★			★								★	★	★						★				
	★	★							★		★	★	★		★	★		★	★			★				★					★	★							★			

Our thanks to ...

Helen Williams, early years mathematics consultant
Jean Millar, family numeracy consultant
Fran Mosley, primary mathematics teacher and author